The Mexican Man in His Backyard

The Mexican Man
in His Backyard

stories & essays

Stephen D. Gutierrez

**Roan
Press**
ROANPRESS.COM

COLOPHON

body type is Zocalo by Cyrus Highsmith

monospace type is Elementa Pro by Mindaugas Strockis

interior design & typeset by Joshua Lurie-Terrell » flavors.me/jlt

cover art by Marilyn Torchin

cover design by Beth Spencer

author photograph by Monica Michelle

Acknowledgments

Of course, acknowledgments, the customary brag sheet of our business, are a funny thing; more than just a nod to those who published us, they are a championing of the American literary scene. Beyond the obligation to mention these magazines, newspapers and anthologies, I feel deeply indebted to them for keeping my spirit alive. In alphabetical order, then, are the publications in which these pieces first appeared.

elimae — "The Spot"
Fiction International — "The World Came Crashing Down On My Wife"
PALABRA: A Magazine of Chicano & Latino Literary Art — "The River in My City"
Redwood Coast Review — "The Big Fresno Fair"
River Teeth — "At the Drive-in with My Brother" and "Homage to the Champ"
San Francisco Chronicle — "The Mexican Man in His Backyard"
Santa Monica Review — "Lucky Guys Forever" as part of a longer story called "The Lucky Guys Saga"
TalkArts — "Song for You"
Third Coast — "La Muerte Hace Tortillas"
ZYZZYVA — "My Good Gray Morning"

"At the Drive-in with My Brother" was reprinted in *The River Teeth Reader*.

"The River in My City" was reprinted in *New California Writing 2013* (Heyday Books).

I would like to thank Marilyn Torchin for the use of her artwork on the cover and Beth Spencer for her indispensable help.

Contents

The Big Fresno Fair

I was living in Fresno and inviting my mom and aunt to visit us when they could. They came up often, on the train, disembarking at the charming station in downtown Fresno. I met them under the quaint tile roof, greeting them on the platform before driving them home, my mom calling out, "Yoo-hoo," waving me down, and my aunt lugging a bag behind her, complaining all the way.

"Get in the car, Stephen," my mother said. "*Hay cholos* around here."

"*Ay*, don't be so prejudiced," my aunt said. "It's just like home, LA."

"It is, isn't it?" I said, as we sat stopped in front of a taqueria. Brown buildings blended into the landscape. In LA, the working poor toiled in factories, not fields. Otherwise, the two cities shared a lot. I liked them both, these places where lower-middle-class Mexicans, like us, could feel good.

"Americans," my mother reminded me, taking it in. "*Mira nomas,* look at how Mexican it is."

But my aunt checked her. "See, Jo, it's Mexican this, Mexican that. But everywhere you go, you want to see where the Mexicans live."

"It's true. I love my people," she said, staring out the window. "But they're so poor. I feel sorry for them."

"Don't be so condescending," I said. "We're no better."

Then she agreed. "We're not, are we? Just poor Mexicans, too."

My aunt said nothing. She was the younger one: The rebel who had been a "career girl" into her late twenties, daring the barrio to call her an old maid, working as a secretary for a corporation and saving enough money to travel.

She went to Mexico. Mesmerized the natives. "The women stared

3

at me like I was nuts, and the men, too! I was wearing capris!"

She went to Hawaii. Broke a few hearts there. "They asked me to dance all night, those guys! But Bev got drunk and we had to cut it short! Crazy Bev!"

When she came back, she met him, Uncle Eddie, a *tejano* with a booming laugh and a love for fishing and good tequila, and her, of course! She got married and slipped into the life of us, giving birth to three boys and living in a nice house in San Gabriel. She tagged along with my mom everywhere. They visited me because they liked Fresno.

She was the hip one. She nudged me all the time.

We rolled into the driveway. My wife came out and helped with the bags. Then we made dinner and sat around talking. My kid toddled around. Those were good days, everybody happy, everybody content. Those visits were fun.

Fall stung the air. The scent of fields drifted into our living room. If it wasn't true, you could imagine it, *campesinos* working the rows and rich, ripe fruit piling up on the ground. Fresno was enchanted and great.

We loved Fresno. Nobody complained, really.

On the third day of their vacation, my mom said, "Let's go to the fair!" She spotted the ad in the newspaper. A bunch of grapes hung under a trellis that spelled out FRESNO.

We prepared to go, my wife staying home because she taught a class at the university that night, and my son buckled in, strapped into his car seat, secured in the back. We took off. We drove the streets to The Big Fresno Fair.

The fairgrounds are on the southeast side of town, a neighborhood with a history of its own, tough and proud. The streets are dark, the houses pleasant, not-too-shabby tract homes with additions and nicely tended lawns. Sometimes an eyesore blights the block.

"I think Joe lives here," my mom said, referring to a relative of ours who lived in town. I didn't know him.

"Around here, somewhere."

"He does, doesn't he?" my aunt said. We stopped in the middle of the block. It looked like any number of streets in LA, any of those streets in Rosemead, Montebello, Alhambra, Pico Rivera; it looked like my neighborhood back home, with an extra sadness. It seemed a little older.

"The Ferris wheel, how pretty," my mom said.

The Ferris wheel circled in the night, brightly lit, neon streaks staying.

I like the sights of fairs; I like the sounds of fairs. I liked it all, walking around with my aunt and mom, Ben strapped in the stroller, wide-eyed and amazed.

We ate fair food and then fair dessert and kept walking around. We explored the big buildings with the gems and flowers and the livestock in the pens. We gazed into the eyes of the cows, waiting for answers. When they gave none, we laughed. Ben pointed to a ride, and we put him in a big orange fish, watching him go round. He shrieked with glee. His balled-up fists shook.

Then it was time to go home. We decided to call it a night. We stood on the concourse, watching the people. On the midway, *la gente del valle* had fascinated us, farmworkers spending their money on crazy games to impress their girlfriends, who hooked onto their tooled leather belts. Whole families carted stuffed animals bigger than any of them and beamed. When I bumped into a man in charge of a brood, I apologized; he gave me a smile. The fair atmosphere worked on us all.

Cholos sauntered past the booths with girlfriends clinging to them, but dove into a game on the sudden, pulling out wads of cash from baggy pockets. They acted cool with each other; bikers strolled the lanes, impressing their ladies with their own acumen.

Blacks from the maligned west side blended in, sporting jackets from their high school. Nobody warred.

The Big Fresno Fair calmed. Peace entered into the night, and anybody caught stupid would be thrown out. Cops patrolled the grounds. On walkie-talkies, security kept in constant touch. A recent stabbing in Fresno wouldn't ruin it.

Everybody enjoyed the fair.

It was time to head out. Then they started pouring in, kids from a different group, streaming through the turnstiles onto the concourse. They came in a horde, the hip-hop generation in numbers, kid after kid looking so severely disconnected they scared you, stepping in through the gate after the pat-down search, scowling on the concrete expanse, waiting to hook up with partners. Chicks, clumped together, swaggeringly bitched about the fucking looks somebody had given them.

Old-time *cholos* stepped aside, gathering their families. The tired and beaten didn't have the energy to confront them. They didn't want to save face. They wanted to get out of there.

"Let's get the hell out of here," my mother said, "this is too much, this place."

"Yeah, Steve, it's a little rowdy now," my aunt said.

We stood by the bathrooms watching the kids come in. Cops followed them with their eyes. Tough, mean kids taking over the fair, spreading and talking.

"Fuck him."

"That bitch don't know..."

Canned words came out of mouths twisted in anger. Eyes sought enemies to lay into.

"I'll beat his fucking ass."

We walked on. Behind us the fair streamed in violently bright colors. People screamed on rides and lights flashed.

"Did you see those two kids?" my mother said, when we got outside.

"Yeah, I did! The two nerds?"

"Yeah," my aunt laughed with us.

Pooling their money at the entrance, they had been spotted. Two nerds, a chubby Chicano and a pimply white kid, customized for the evening with slicked-back hair and all the right clothes worn all wrong.

They reminded me of me. But I loved them for that.

"Do we have enough to get in?" came out of one.

"Count it, fool! We might have to break in!"

"That would be crazy!"

"Sometimes you have to do things anarchic."

"Retro juvenile you mean."

"Whatever." They plotted their mischief. It meant finding a way in and using it.

"Did you hear them?" my aunt asked.

"Some of it."

"What were they saying?"

"That they're going to get in free and be bad, bad boys."

We all started laughing, watching them skirt the entrance to another side of the fair.

They disappeared into the shadows.

A thug group approached us.

"Then I told that bitch I don't need no shit from you. Know what I'm saying?"

"Fuck that bitch. Look at them bitches over there. Who those fools with them? They mad dogging us?"

"Hurry up, Stephen," my mother said, elbowing me. "Let's get out of here. Let's go home."

"Yeah, it's kind of rough around here, Steve," my aunt said, whispering under her breath. We had reached the parking lot and were crossing the street soon.

"It is," I said. "And where were your Mexicans, Mom?"

"Everywhere," she said, "spending their hard-earned money, like fools."

"But having a good time," my aunt said.

"Having a good time, I guess," my mom said. "But those kids of theirs, this new generation, *ay*, what are we gonna do?"

"Nothing," I said. "Wait until the poets arise and make sense of them."

"Will they come from them?"

"Never," I said, "they'll come from the ones who talk straight."

"And wear their pants up to their waists," my aunt said, stopping at the car and laughing. She imitated the two nerds back there talking.

"Look at the Ferris wheel," I said, "it's still spinning." I unbuckled my kid in his stroller and began to put him in his car seat.

"Hey, you, Mister Ben," I told him.

He waved a fist at me.

I put it in my mouth and bit it. "Learn to speak around your fist. Don't mumble."

"What are you talking about there," my mom said. She was standing beside me at the door.

"Everything," I said, "important to me."

Ben laughed. I kissed his hand and gave it back to him.

"Okay, Ben, you're all set," I said.

"Are you ready to go, then?" my mother said.

"I'm ready," I said.

We paused for a second looking over the car at the Ferris wheel. Its radiant spokes kept turning in a circle of light.

The Mexican Man in His Backyard
A Fable of Sorts

The Mexican man parked his car in his driveway, blocking it, and sat in his backyard watching TV. He ignored me.

I saw him from the sidewalk. I came back from jogging and saw him in his chaise longue, relaxing. I always wanted him to say something to me, but he never did, his back to me, to the world.

The Mexican man seemed to enjoy his small black and white TV more than most people enjoy sports, sex, banana splits. He seemed proud of it, defiantly proud, adjusting the antenna with quick, jerky movements of his worn, brown hands.

But maybe I am making too much of his simplicity. Maybe he just couldn't afford a bigger TV. But there in his backyard, he watched the small black and white TV into the night, comfortably reclined, content. I saw him many times, wanted to make his acquaintance, kept walking.

The Mexican man's wife sometimes joined him. She sat in an upright chair next to him, the sturdy, wooden chair that had been lifted out of the kitchen and placed on the ground by him, the Mexican man slapping the seat clean before he permitted her to sit down. Then he forgot about her, getting lost in his team, the Dodgers. He always seemed to be following the Dodgers and their chase.

I caught the voice of an announcer in Spanish. *"Los Dodgers están jugando con mucho..."* He sported a bumper sticker on his '68 Impala in the driveway, *L.A. Dodgers!*

I was new to Fresno. I felt a kinship based on this interest. Plus the way he sniffed the air. Plus the way he kicked at things in his yard, dirt clods and crap. He reminded me of my grandfather roaming his grounds in LA, just as modest a patch of earth, but kept right.

I lived down the street from him in a corner house, facing traffic and the accidents on Clinton and Maroa, a busy intersection called jinxed by the Highway Patrol.

His wife put up with as much baseball as she could. Then she went inside.

Still, she must have enjoyed watching the games with him, because I gleaned a certain satisfaction on her face as she tramped across the lawn, as if they had snuck away and savored a forbidden pleasure meant for them only.

Maybe she was thinking of sex in their younger days.

The Mexican man cleared his throat and said little. When he spoke, it was in Spanish, mellifluous and short. I heard him around the house. I lived in back of him, two doors down. It was a long yard that separated us, punctuated by his house and the house of the Indian next to him.

The Indian was a Mexican from Guanajuato. One day he invited me over.

I had to climb a wall to get there. "Wetbacking it," I said to myself, humorously. I hopped up onto the top.

It was short, not too high; a stone wall, with a crumbling top. I had been pulling weeds in the backyard, standing up to recover before dipping back down again, wiping my sweat off. He called to me, waving me over.

I made shrugging motions, he persisted, and I sailed over the wall to his house.

I must have look famished, because he invited me to dinner, and in fact I hadn't eaten yet. I was hungry. The sky was softly hued, gray around the edges and in the center, dabbed with white. It was a kind and receptive Fresno day, Sunday, peaceful, uncrowded. I decided to accept.

I went back home and told my wife.

"Jackie, I've been invited to the neighbors' for some *carne asada*. Want to come?"

"What? *Carne asada*? Who?" She had never noticed the neighbors before. They kept to themselves.

She decided to stay home. She's as shy around Mexicans as they are shy around her.

I climbed back over the wall and into their yard.

"*Hola!*" I shouted out.

I sat on a long bench set in the dirt. Dirt made up the backyard, with little shade or vegetation, no grass. It was hot enough, with the Fresno sun still burning in the sky. He didn't seem to mind, this Indian guy barely talking to me because he didn't know English, but wanting to extend his hospitality to me.

He kept trying. He cooked his *asada* on a barbecue, a small hibachi, and made conversation.

He was from Guanajuato, the same state my people are from, and it was good to know that. He had come a while back, with his wife and daughter, a baby girl inside now taking a nap. They had worked hard. They had struggled.

"This," he said, "is my house."

He pointed to his house in back of us. It was the same frame house owned by the Mexican, only smaller, as if it had been duplicated in miniature. Not exactly miniature, but reduced. It was neat. There were whitewashed boards and painted shutters. There were flowers carefully planted around the house and a well-manicured lawn. Everything was kept up and done. He swept the driveway often, you could tell, and only the backyard needed work. He would get to that later.

He explained all this to me, doing his best as I sat on the bench. It was hard. He spoke really poor English. I speak really bad Spanish.

13

We made an effort, and then he took me inside. After the meal, which was simple and good—*carne asada* served on corn tortillas with chile, a dab of rice on the side, and beans, eaten off plates on our laps, real plates, not paper, with cold Mexican beers handy—he insisted I see his place. So I said OK, as I was curious and wanted to honor him. He took me through the side door, and we entered a small, dark room with a bed pushed up against the wall—his daughter's, who was waking up now from her nap, a little girl of about two or three years old.

I walked on into the living room. A curtained cubicle; a little bigger. It was clean and presentable, something he had worked hard for. He showed me his kitchen, gave me a peek at their bedroom, and edged me into *el baño*, which provided comfort, too. It was up to date.

He flushed and smiled.

His wife was a simply groomed woman in a thick black skirt who kept serving us food outside, ministering to our needs, saying little, until he dismissed her to the inside. Now she sat in the corner with her child. She hardly said anything; she kept her face down. But when she spoke and acted, it was with sturdiness and force. He was courteous and polite with her, respectful.

He opened up some more as we went outside.

He had been helped in his transactions with the authorities. When some shady character had tried to cheat him on his way to owning the house, Alfonso, *el señor* next door, had stepped in and set it right. He owed a lot to him. He was a good neighbor. Did I know him?

No. A little bit. Once again, I thanked him for his wonderful meal and went home, this time walking around the corner instead of climbing over the wall. I had a full belly.

"Jackie, it was great..." I burst into our house. I told my wife about the incredible neighborhood that we were a part of.

"Really." She couldn't believe it, but I convinced her.

"We might buy around here."

"Okay, if you say so." She was too busy with our own child to pay me much mind, nursing him.

But I was excited. "Yeah, we can send him to a multicultural school." I knew the mantra.

I had been a substitute teacher for a season. But life fell into its normal rhythm.

I put the plan on hold. I concentrated on surviving and appreciating daily life on Maroa.

The Indian waved to me over the wall in the back.

The Mexican man kept to himself, stuck to his routine, hardly bothered with me, with anybody. When an accident occurred on my street and required my translating, which I wasn't capable of, I rushed to his house, sensing that the victim of the accident, a Mexican farmworker in a battered pickup truck with stickers on the side, *Radio Campesino, 95.9*, was going to get shafted. I knocked on his door.

I heard him approaching.

I waited in fear.

He said, "*Sí?*" then, quickly changing his tune, "Yes?" and proceeded to help us in the street.

When it was over, the Mexican man went back in his house, closed the door and drew the curtains. Later that night, he sat in his backyard, turned on the TV and watched the Dodgers. He continued to ignore me. He didn't care.

My Good Gray Morning

Para Ernesto Trejo
Siempre

Los dos poetas showed up on my lawn in the early morning, Ernesto Trejo and Omar Salinas. They loomed in my window walking across the fog in purposeful strides, bumping up against each other in their eagerness to reach my door.

"Jackie! Ernesto Trejo and Omar Salinas are here! They're at the door!"

"What!"

So I rushed to open it.

And there before me stood *los dos poetas* in the fog, hanging back out of politeness and courtesy, an old-world sense of formality.

"Come in, *entra!*" I shouted.

And then *los dos poetas* made themselves comfortable in my home.

"Steve! Jackie!" They greeted us both, and then they both lumbered through my house taking off their coats, heading toward the warmth of my wood-stoved study, my shabbily rugged comfort zone.

"What are you guys up to?" Jackie asked.

"Nothing, just bothering you," Ernesto sat down with a smile. *Se sentó.*

Y entonces, Omar *comenzó,* clearing his throat and looking around for an ashtray. He started making fidgety movements with his fingers, digital preambles to his smokes.

So then *en esta mañana,* we let Omar out the door to smoke in the backyard.

Era gray and foggy *afuera.*

The heavy gray fog settled on him. He looked wet and cold.
He looked miserable and unloved.

He stood alone in the universe under a tree.

Omar se fumó un cigarrillo debajo de mi árbol, y Ernesto, majestic
in the gray, smiled.

We got down to business. "Steve, I got a proposition for you."

"What?"

"Teach creative writing, fiction, just fiction for me."

"OK, when do I start?"

"Monday." He filled me in on the details.

The details were more somber than this story implies.

A few years later, the hint of massacre would be confirmed.
Those errant cells in Ernesto Trejo's body would win, and we
would visit him in the Belmont Memorial Cemetery in Fresno,
Omar and I would, standing over his grave in tottering silence.

"Era un poeta," Omar would say, *"un poeta con mucho corazón."*
He would touch his own heart patting for a cigarette, and then he
would smoke one, gazing off into the distance over the ivy fence
at the few cars passing on the road.

I said a prayer over Ernesto Trejo's grave, *este vato* who engineered
me a job, and then got on my knees and pulled apart the few weeds
already twisting over the headstone.

Underneath me on the cold earth read:

ERNESTO TREJO
PLACE A DYING SPARROW

IN MY HANDS
MY SOUL WILL FIND A TREE TO PERCH ON
1950 — 1991

"¿Ernesto?"

"¿*Qué?*"

"¿*Qué dice usted, señor? ¿Cómo es en el otro lado?*"

"*Es muy suave, Esteban. Es muy fino.*"

Ernesto Trejo whispered through the trees around us, turning on his side to get some more sleep when we stayed too long, releasing a bird from the tree next to us.

And I watched it fly into the sky.

Ernesto Trejo, *el mexicano* transplanted to the United States in high school, mastering English in an exchange program in Fresno and staying for college to study economics, discovered himself as a poet. He plugged into the local literary scene in earnest, revealing talent and will, and marched on: graduated from the University of Iowa Writers Workshop with an MFA in poetry, lived in Mexico for a year with his wife Diane and their new family—two kids, one girl and one boy—declined a job with the Mexican government at the highest level of diplomatic service, and then returned to Fresno, by strange coincidence a larger echo of his own hometown in Mexico, Fresnillo.

"I'll see you, Ernesto, *ya me voy.*"

"OK."

I got up off my knees.

Ernesto Trejo *gané empleo con el colegio en Fresno,* Fresno City College, and involved himself in literary activities around town, championing certain Chicano poets he deemed worthy, encouraging select Chicano prose writers he thought necessary, and imprinting on me a fine sense of my own importance when he signed his book to me at the Fig Garden Bookstore a few months before he died.

For Steve, Jackie, & Ben,

Hope you like these poems. Thank you for teaching my class. Fresno needs you.

Love, Ernesto.

And I could have cried right there. Perhaps I did even turn around and choke.

I had been passed over by the people in power at the big state university in Fresno for a job in creative writing, my writing deemed too paltry and insignificant for such titans as occupied the university seats then, two giants of the contemporary literary scene just too massive to contemplate without fearing their august selves and trembling in disbelief that I even dared lift a pencil in that town, a fucked-up show of arrogance and stupidity in my humble and Mexican opinion. I was made to feel small. I hadn't even received a postcard acknowledging my existence, a response to my application, what I minimally expected. Maybe an interview. Nothing. I felt humiliated and shamed. But Ernesto Trejo redeemed me in my own eyes, Mexican to Chicano, validating my own worth.

He reached out a hand from the grave.

"¡Cuídate, Steve! ¡Cuída a Omar, también!"

He saw us into our car before lying down again for sleep.

And Ernesto Trejo spoke Spanish around his friends, Omar Salinas and other Mexicans from around town, Omar a fine Mexican-American poet in his own right, who came in out of the cold that day into my gray den, *el* Omar did, rocking on his heels in my study, laughing, cracking up, blowing into his hands, just at the goddamned *frío* outside.

Hacía frío outside, and Omar Salinas followed Ernesto Trejo out my door to the car parked at the curb. They waded through the gray in the morning, Omar *también* a troubadour of the fields and the loneliness of being an outcast Mexican, a Sanger native whose bouts with schizophrenia informed his poetry and life. He had sad, terrible eyes, shook his head at the waste around him, and kept up his cheer with the comfort Ernesto Trejo provided him, the company of other Fresno poets, and coffee.

Ernesto Trejo paused at my threshold before taking off, giving me final instructions in perfect English with the slightest of Mexican accents. He warned me of betrayers and haters, of those who would sabotage my efforts to be included, especially those coveting the job he was handing over to me, the job in creative writing considered a plum.

"I want you," he said, looking me straight in the eye, and Ernesto Trejo set my life on a certain course that morning.

He pushed me out into the world.

He gave me a chance.

Este vato who was hired because of affirmative action, despite his excellence, that being the tool to wedge him in, gave me the help I needed.

He told me to go see the dean who was cool, the dean amenable to us all, Chicanos, *mexicanos transplantados*, Mexican Americans, *gente todos de la raza unida, cósmico y cómico*, laughing as we went out. "Give him your best, Steve, just don't tell him what you're really like."

"That would be bad," I said, "wouldn't it?"

And they both nodded sagely, *estos cabrones, los dos poetas en Fresno, mis amigos mexicanos.*

Part Two

Lucky Guys Forever
The Affair of the Brown Ten-Speed

Lucky Guys Forever is proudly sponsored by your neighborhood hamburger stand, LUCKY GUYS!

Lonely on Sundays? Try *Lucky Guys!* Commerce's latest hot spot for conviviality and comfort. Invite Carmen, drag Jaime there. You'll enjoy our new dining facility with its plush leather seating, lighted chandelier lamps and heavenly aromas wafting in from the kitchen. Try our new kids menu—if you're a kid! Enjoy our moderate temperature in winter and summer! Fully air-conditioned and heated! And remember, families welcome, as we are *Lucky Guys* extending a hand toward you!

(Coupons available. Look for them in your friendly weekly newspaper, The Commerce Tribune, *right under the smiling faces of Dimitri and George, our master chefs!)*

Once upon a time in my hometown of Commerce stuck down there in Los Angeles, the wider area with the same concrete and asphalt extending in all directions to the next town, a poor boy appeared on a brown ten-speed riding to Lucky Guys at night. His name was Herrera. He was dark, with big, bulging frog eyes and a lambskin-lined jacket he wore all seasons of the year. We'd see him eating his meal there in the corner. He was trouble.

I recognized him from a long time ago. He had gone to the same school I had gone to in my old neighborhood before we moved to Rosewood, the better part of Commerce. He had always been trouble, a smartass, defiant. Now it was all coming apart for him; it was all catching up to him. There were rumors.

He sat there glowering at us younger guys making asses of ourselves, but didn't say anything, generally. Ordering our food at the counter, we were stupid, but didn't pay much attention to him, either. We didn't know him well, only as a guy in the neighborhood, the larger 'hood. He was out of our league.

One night he spoke...

I was going to write a particularly bad story of Lucky Guys, but nothing bad happened at Lucky Guys, and that is the honest truth. I was going to have him call me out, and I would stand up to him, but that didn't happen at all.

What happened was this: There was this guy, dimly remembered, who used to hang out at Lucky Guys. His name was Herrera. He owned a magnificent ten-speed, bought in the days when any ten-speed meant something.

I mean, do you remember the days when ten-speeds first became popular, really popular, among the masses, the working class, the regular folks like you and me, the people on a budget? No longer the bicycle of choice among serious riders and bike nuts only; everybody rode one, suddenly. Everybody hunched and pedaled.

Ten-speed mania gripped the country.

This is the time I'm talking about, and Herrera figures in there with his own ten-speed to brag about, I know for a fact on good authority, the rumor mill constantly turning, when he had nothing more to say. When he had nothing else to lean on, he turned back to that time of glorious rapture, of ten-speed heaven, of unspeakable happiness.

So a few years before I started hanging out at Lucky Guys and learning about myself and others, learning the stuff teenagers do, ten-speeds became the craze. They were the must-have item overnight.

They were ungainly, took a while to master. But once steadied, wow! Big wheels, wraparound handlebars like rams' horns, skinny racing seats, ten-speeds not in name only but in fact. Levers at your command, brakes so delicate you need be careful. Ten-speeds!

And the colors! Vibrant greens, blues, reds! Schwinn got in on the business fast and marked its territory with its signature models. The low-budget Varsity was the norm, costly enough already without the frills—a carrying rack, a generator light, an air pump attached to the frame. Right above it stood the noble Continental, lighter, sleeker, smoother—a better ride all around.

They were pretty rare. But my friend got one handed down from his big brother, who stole it from the beach, and that's how we got our Continentals in the neighborhood. It was the canary yellow version with the famous *Schwinn* insignia painted in cursive on the sides. He even registered it at the local police department.

So much in our lives goes on underground.

Lucky Guys went up at about the same time, too, and that was exciting.

That's when Herrera came on the scene for me. That's when for the first, and probably last time in his life, he rode in sync with the times, proud owner of a brand new Varsity.

I watched him ride up. It was with a special care I hadn't seen amongst the most fastidious of us. Then he got off.

He put the kickstand down carefully, parking the bike by the plastic table out in front. He rubbed the seat with a little piece of cloth he pulled out of his back pocket, gently and delicately, as if shining the chrome on a vintage Mercedes worth thousands, or brushing the debris off the Mona Lisa's lip for an untold commission, but doing it out of love, not for filthy lucre. He was in his Levi's, bundled into the always-on, leather-fronted, lambskin-lined jacket. I forget what season it was.

Commerce, all seasons.

He looked over his shoulder at me, sneeringly, it seemed.

I didn't have one, a ten-speed. Later I would get one, a fine Italian ten-speed (well, okay, made in China but with an Italian-sounding name) from Pep Boys, and it would suit me fine. But right now I didn't have one, didn't have the latest thing, and I wasn't bothered by it.

I didn't need to change gears for a long time, or so I thought.

"Hey, Steve."

"What?

"Aren't you going to order?"

"Uh-huh."

My friends called to me but I remained riveted to my spot. I stayed in view of what intrigued me.

"I'll get a burger right now, man. Go inside."

Herrera walked up to the screened window that you ordered at, keeping an eye on his bike. It leaned there perfectly on its kickstand. He ordered out of the side of his mouth.

"I will please have a hamburger, fries, and a coke." He seemed to be inhabited by a whole new spirit. This formidable being spoke a new lingo not common to these parts. He smiled serenely. But out of his self-satisfaction came smugness, too. It was too easy for me to remember the prick I knew.

I measured him in terms of the past, and it wasn't good. It was bad.

He hadn't been kind to me ever. I didn't trust him worth a damn.

Still, he touched me with the regard he showed for his bike. And I have to admit, without assigning too great a significance to it, the color of his bike attracted my curiosity as much as the bike itself and his relationship to it.

The brownness of the bike floored me. It was a rich root beer brown capturing everybody's attention and love. More than a few people owned a Varsity that color, but his relationship to his seemed natural, comfortable, deeper than theirs, than anybody's in the neighborhood.

Victor Herrera is in love with his bike, I thought. Really in love with his bike!

And out of my dim understanding of the world an observation rose in my head to ponder at night before falling asleep, for I considered myself somewhat of a philosopher and privy to deep thoughts, real insight.

Herrera is at the top of his game. He will never do anything greater in his life than what he is doing now, caring for his brand new bike, a root beer brown Schwinn Varsity ten-speed bought at the height of the ten-speed craze.

He should be proud.

He eyed that thing from his seat at the table outside and ate his hamburger absent-mindedly; afterwards, wiping his mouth with his napkin, he double-cleaned his hands on his pants before he straddled the bike and let his hands touch the root beer brown tape of the handlebars.

Then he rode off down the sidewalk past Chuck's Bar and the sales office of the industrial equipment firm anchored at the corner, scarcely paying attention to where he was going; shifting gears, he looked down. Pedaling slowly, legs bowlegged, he almost went off the curb into traffic, and applied the brakes just in time.

He got off his bike and walked it across the street to the next sidewalk.

He was an asshole I didn't like. He bought his bike with some ill-gotten gains, probably, drug profits or from raiding his mother's wallet after the paycheck got cashed, or got it for Christmas when the bonus check came in. I don't know. I don't care.

Everybody had ten-speeds then. So did he.

But it didn't change my attitude towards him.

I watched him disappear down the sidewalk, to Bandini, my old neighborhood, where he still lived.

I stepped up to the window and ordered my meal, or picked up the loaded tray if I already had, and went inside and hung out with the clowns, my friends. (Of course, I wore the biggest, brightest, reddest nose among them, and don't forget that for a second.) I sat with them and laughed or sat glumly for a spell or twirled my thumbs in amusement at the table or stared out the window at nothing or did something else entirely different besides eat like a ravenous teenage boy trying to go unnoticed.

Or walked on home distraught on a sudden impulse. I was given to such fits.

But Herrera is our subject here. We must return to him.

I would see him around town with his bike. Polishing it as he spoke to people, he stood by it proudly. Waving from it, he rode regally. Crashing it in somebody's yard when he was drunk, he cursed it and himself the next day for loving it so much, but lifted it up gently, lovingly, after the rebukes, after all had been said, and brought it back to lustrousness with the soft cloth he carried with him everywhere he went.

I didn't like him. I didn't like him at all.

He sat there one evening in Lucky Guys years later. The bike craze was over now. The ten-speeds were dumped on lawns across the city, casual vehicles no longer holding the allure they once did, passé. And Lucky Guys was getting older and shabbier by the minute.

But this story isn't over with, not by a long shot. I need to tell you more about the fiend Herrera, and why he preyed on me.

...

Nothing bad happened at Lucky Guys, and that is the honest truth. In my story, certain versions are played with, but none of them untrue. That is the virtue of writing imaginative non-fiction. You get to do what the fuck you want.

I, for instance, want to focus on the owners of Lucky Guys right now, a couple of Greeks sharing all duties behind the smudged counter we laid our elbows on after ordering, and waited. They were always busy in the kitchen, laughing, joking with us, a couple of characters, with even more Greeks coming over from the old country to don an apron and do time in the favored hamburger stand—they had an interest in two or three of them in LA, I heard—in Commerce.

But I'm digressing. Let's go back to the main story.

So in my neighborhood lived Victor Herrera, and he rode a ten-speed. He lived in the larger neighborhood of my upbringing, and not my immediate one, so I did not know him well. I did not see him day to day, only upon occasion. But every time I saw him I thought about him for days.

The first time I saw him with his bike was probably in front of the liquor store, picking up some booze to cart away under his arm on his wobbly ten-speed that called attention to itself. But that's neither here nor there. That's not important at all.

Then he ceased being the man about town, the fortunate son with the swagger and Schwinn, and shifted into low. Over the years, the bad habits he picked up consumed him, and he lay wasted in an SRO near downtown, I heard, no longer welcome at home, jobless, friendless, a junkie.

They said the last thing he said was, "Hey, remember the Schwinn ten-speeds? I got one when I was a kid, *ey*. A root beer brown one like all the cool people had. Like me. Like the color of my girlfriend's eyes back then, Sandy. I used to ride that bike all around the neighborhood and take good care of it until I crashed it one night and fucked up the fork. Then I just rode it like regular and it got all fucked up over the years, like everything else, ha! But it was cool, man, having a bike like that when it first came out, like all styling and shit, in Commerce. I even began to talk different, I swear! I had some class for about a week! Ha, ha, ha! Got a light for my *frajo*? I'm kind of down on my luck, man. Got a couple of bucks maybe you could spare for an old homeboy?

31

I'll pay you back, in a little bit, for sure."

He mellowed and died. But the old Victor Herrera rose in my head at times and frightened me.

That would be the same Victor Herrera who rode kingly upon the streets of Commerce and sneered at us all, we who seemed weaker than him. What I considered the cowardly part of his personality, preying on the defenseless and young, those who couldn't fight back or talk up a good game to counter his hurtfulness, always won out. It predominated for a good long time before he succumbed to his own weakness, his own destiny.

I'm just trying to manage an excuse for my dislike of him, after establishing him as a somewhat sympathetic figure. He was! But before that, no! He wasn't! He was a prick.

I hated him. I was afraid of him, for one thing. I kept thinking he would bring something up that would embarrass me. He would burrow into my past and, in front of my friends, humiliate me. He was that kind of guy.

My answer would be to cry. And at my age, I couldn't afford to do that anymore, no? I couldn't be pegged a crybaby when I had been somewhat of a bawler back then.

Back then. Let me go there, as they say, and make an attempt at absolute clarification.

When we attended the same school—and it was a beautiful school, oh my!—he cast a long shadow across its courtyard. Otherwise, it was sublimely gorgeous to my untrained eye. Bandini Elementary School, made of red brick turned dark and venerable, and inside, a long hallway entrancing me, note in hand, walking to the principal's office with a piss stain on my crotch and scared eyes bubbled out. No matter!

The hall was beautiful. A combined odor of chalk and sweat filled it, and a faint yellow light suffused it, reflecting off the highly polished floor. Set into classroom doors, the bumpy, frosted windows let out further light, ghostly blobs that rested in the air before I blinked them away. How I loved that place!

Victor Herrera wasn't a good part of it. He led a set that made fun of me, my big ears that stuck out at an acute 90° angle from my head. Before the plastic surgery that "corrected" them in my eighth year, and none too well (but leave that at that. That is another story, and a long, painful one), I was the butt of their jokes. They loved to see me coming.

They loved to stand atop a table under a big tree and point at me, and laugh, calling me all the usual names, only with more vehemence than most. They were, okay, the doomed, with their own problems at home, with their own self-hating images generated from stupid and cruel parents, but fuck them! I say that now, disregarding my present knowledge.

Fuck them then and fuck them now! Christian charity be damned! Compassion comes only for those I can respect.

Victor Herrera was especially mocking. "Hey, big ears! Did you wake up like that or order special delivery? Dumbo ears for Halloween? It's not even, *ey*! Check him out!"

I hastened by him.

He later rolled up his sleeve and, well, you know the story. You know how that one turns out.

He paved his own path to hell and...

He got into my head back then. He made me feel awful with feelings of freakishness so profound they still linger in me.

He branded me with shame.

"Who the fuck am I to even live?" I told myself.

It was shitty being me. It was rising up in me again, all these feelings.

Adolescence hit me hard. It hit me in harder ways than youth: my nose grew out of control, really big, and my poorly reconstructed ears still got made fun of at times, unexpectedly and suddenly, like when hanging out on a street corner with some fellas drinking a beer, trying to do the teenage thing without hearing about the past. (There, I told it! That story, a little bit. Enclosed in parentheses is the only real place I feel safe with it. I wish I could live in parentheses forever.) And I fought, and I cried, and I sulked, and I brooded, and I dealt with many things in my life.

My old man wasn't well. He suffered the effects of a terrible mind-robbing disease, but worse than that, for me, at least, a selfish teenager, was the fact that he was known in the neighborhood to be crazy, the street diagnosis of his complex disease. Mildly lunatic at best. Not quite there. Weird.

I couldn't accept his difference, ever, but when it manifested in full-blown dementia, I cried inside. I sought relief in dark fantasy.

I didn't want to live. That was my teenage misery.

Lucky Guys Forever picks up at this point.

With magnificent craftsmanship, I have brought you here. (Good for a thing or two besides running myself down, I allow myself a pat on the back and hope you share my enthusiasm for me. If not me, who? If not you, who? Love yourself, reader, and I'll consider myself successful in this enterprising piece of writing.) Herrera is center stage.

I tried to avoid him. It was for a very simple reason. He was capable of tormenting me, and I knew it, and he knew it, and everybody around us knew it. Knew it as sure as the sun would set the next day and invite the stars to their usual party in the sky. Everybody knew it, standing around in that dingy old place called (and hold fast, reader, as I'm a-gettin' going now, and once the true spirit of fiction grabs me, pert' near impossible to stop)...

Lucky Fellers

The saloon doors winged to a close on
creaky hinges. The bartender cleaned
glasses behind the bar, and the grill
in the back lay silent. Partners of the
principals shuffled cards and cared to
look up only when necessary.

It was coming down, this old showdown
between the two ancient foes, Herrera
and Champion.

"Don't 'spect it can be put off much longer."

"'deed not. There's gonna be blood spilled."

"Shut yer lips, sodbuster, and play cards."

"As you like it."

Herrera sat in his favorite corner eating a hamburger, glowering at me. But rather than settling on me, he took in the whole room in a general survey, doling out his disgust in equal measure.

He followed that up with a frown and a renewed interest in his french fries.

Burp! He let out a big one.

Nothing recommended itself to change, which is a fancy way of saying:

Nothing happened; life (I'll tell you this. I don't care that you've heard it before) went on.

But there did arise a new tension in Lucky Guys. Because of me... there is no use lying about it; life went on.

There's no big climactic scene in my fiction, in my essay, in my whatever-you-want-to-call-this.

There's no scene that looks like this:

Herrera got up from his booth and sauntered over to us. Standing over our booth, bowlegged in his Levi's and picking at his teeth with a toothpick, he began to make fun of me, starting with my father, whom he called a mean name reserved for the disabled, and landing on me.

"Dumbo ears. You still got them Dumbo ears?" He reached out to touch them, and that's when I stood.

"Fuck you, Herrera. You stupid shit. I heard you couldn't even handle the continuation school, you're so fucking stupid. Dropped out like an idiot. Is that true? Are you that fucking stupid? Like your whole fucking family with your fucking food stamps and unemployment checks and crying babies. 'Why do these people still breed?' my mother asked me the other night. 'Why?'"

He looked at me dumbfounded, and we stepped outside to settle it, Herrera motioning me with a shoulder as if we were going to kick it pleasantly, like we did in Commerce when things needed to be settled. "Let's take it outside, dude. I'll show you what I know."

"Should only take a second then, dumb fuck." Though older than me, I wasn't afraid of him anymore. I was a hot teenager with daring in my veins.

I mocked his love on the way out. "Piece of shit Varsity." I rattled the handlebars for effect, "little bitch for bitches," and readied myself.

It was on.

```
Lucky Fellers (cont.)

Finally he stood up from his meal in the far cor-
ner he called his own, and approached the center
of the saloon. He clanged across the floor in
```

his spurs and boots. Set his hat back and stared
across the room at Champion.

That would be me, for I am the Champion, and
don't you ever forget it.

My friends cleared a circle. The wind rattled
the casements in the saloon; the sawdust blew up
in fitful gusts, like small tumbleweeds hurry-
ing across the floor. I kicked one aside and approached my man.

I was wearing black, with a spinning sheriff's
star on my chest that sent out sparks. Black
shirted, black jeaned, with my silver spurs
clinking on the heels of my black boots, I was
looking bad. I lowered my hat over my eyes, adjusted it solemnly. Then I just grabbed it and
flung it aside.

It turned out to be a pizza flying across the
room and, smashing against the wall, whirled the
whole saloon into a party, a festive party!

Ya-hoo! The kid does it again! Champion ain't no
champion for no reason at all!

He gets us out of this mess without blood, vio-
lence, or a change of underwear.

Nothing bad happened that night at Lucky Guys. It was even a
better night than most, with a good feeling amongst everybody.

The Greeks flipped burgers expertly and kept up a yammering
conversation settling the pussy question once and for all. "You
getting enough pussy?" a Greek asked, over his smoking grill.

"Naw, naw naw, he not get enough, he so hungry for it." His brother answered for him, busy with the drinks.

"But you?" He picked out another one of us standing at the counter.

"No, no, no, he gets too much." In the Greek equation, only so much pussy to go around! The hogs knew it as clearly as the starved.

There had to be a better way.

"Let the pussy come to you! Don't go to the pussy so much! Don't scare the pussy and then none for him. You don't get the pussy. You lie! You play with the meat!" He whipped out a big hot dog and flipped it up and down before throwing it on the grill.

"No pussy for you! Only the hand!"

"Only the hand." They both came to this solemn conclusion.

We laughed it up and sat at our table eating heartily. He ate his own meal in the corner, barely noticing us after a while, and nothing happened.

We kept to ourselves and remained cheerful. It was another night at Lucky Guys.

But Victor Herrera had made me aware, aware of something I wasn't before. His whore, his old sturdy whore, could take him down with her any time she wanted. And whatever that means, I don't know.

In our fight, I would knock down his bike, and that would be symbolic, too. Because she had knocked me down a few times now I would wreak vengeance on her.

He would stand there, agape, as I pummeled his bike, mangled it with super-hero strength to the wide-eyed astonishment of my friends on the sidewalk.

He would say nothing. The Greeks would close the window and turn off the lights in the kitchen. "Why are we working so hard?" they'd ask, and throw a big party for everybody.

They happened once in a while. They were good.

"Let's call up the girls, my friends! Let's drink the ouzo!"

This part of *Lucky Guys Forever* ends in a party, I'm convinced.
Lucky Guys Forever would mean nothing without a mad, mad
revel at the end, a crowning celebration in there somewhere.

...

Nothing happened, and that's the truth.

I didn't like him, but I backed off from my vengeful cravings, my
revenge fantasies. I did this because I felt drawn to him in his
loneliness, sitting there in the corner after his abrupt scan of us.
He settled his hate on the only person he really knew, himself,
and I felt for him.

It spread out from him in certain waves, like the feeling you get
around truly nice people who warm you. Only with him it was the
opposite and directed back at himself. Struggling with it, he even
permitted himself the merest smile when he got up to leave and
passed our table, catching my eye, it seemed to me—absorbed in
my own pile of french fries—for something important he needed
to say but couldn't.

"I'm sorry."

"That's okay." I didn't say in return, but gave him the chin up salu-
tation we used to say *Everything's all right, brother.*

Everything's cool. I saw a little bit of myself in him. And I knew
he needed only one thing, love.

Nothing else would do. Nothing else was worthy of me.

We had to help each other, the wounded. This came upon me
in a flash, without premeditation. Later I would learn what it
was called, an epiphany. And in that state, feeling much for him
and the world, with myself included, I turned away for a second.

Then I brought a closed fist to my mouth and lowered my head in an act of almost-burping but really crying, watching his sad ass walking out the door and seeing her there so nakedly, his lonely woman barely upright on the sidewalk in front of Lucky Guys, kickstanded crookedly, with the seat torn and twisted and the handlebar tape shredded to bits, an old whore coming undone, ready for her last ride, with lover atop her.

"That motherfucker's crazy," I said, to no one in particular. When they looked at me with astonishment, I got up from the table and went home.

La Muerte Hace Tortillas

My father was fine. There was nothing wrong with him, nothing. Just the opposite. Even with the rumors flying about him—that there was something, just a little something off there; just a little something to wonder about—he towered over most fathers because he was strong and tall and handsome. He held his own in our neighborhood and made me proud of him. I upheld his noble quality in my mind, even as I was washed in shame from an early age because of his deficiencies.

He was different. People told me something else after he died, mostly relatives who had known him for a long time but also some of his old-time buddies from work whom I hardly knew. "Your father was very nice. He had the manners of a prince. Something about him was very courteous and correct. Nice. Kind. Gentle. Decent."

He was fine. But not in certain departments.

When it came to cussing, my father wasn't one of the champions. He couldn't compete with the best on the block, with the masters in the neighborhood. Fathers of the boys I hung out with, those guys—those pot-bellied men smelling of cigarettes and beer on a Saturday afternoon in a garage, hanging around a workbench. I'm talking about the pros here, the men I looked up to. Aggravated in my sense of my father's incompleteness, I saw in them versions of absolute manhood. They were the real thing, the real deal.

The fuckmeisters, that's who they were. "Fuck fuck fuck," they said, in their manly domains, cussing out the world—their fucking bosses, the goddamn fucking hammer that had slammed their thumbs, the fucking government, the fucking wetbacks in the alley behind them, the fucking Okies at work, the fucking niggers, the fucking Japs, the fucking you-name-it Jews/communists/rich bastards, anybody remotely threatening them. Anybody responsible for their stunted lives. "Fuck them!" They cursed the neighbors next door playing the stereo too loud.

"Fuck!" It came trilling out of their pinched lips like a glorious afterbirth. At whoever. At whatever.

"Fuck those fucking assholes."

My dad didn't know how to sing this song, I thought, this F-song, couldn't even strike a minor note in it—one fucking F-word was all I needed—and it set him apart that he didn't know. He didn't cuss properly. He said *chingao*. He muttered a quiet damn.

He had other things on his mind, maybe. Big things.

But I was waiting, waiting for him to show me.

...

It came again, a payday, and my father and I were cruising down Atlantic Boulevard on a Saturday afternoon. We're going into the heart of East LA to Builder's Emporium on Third Street.

It's right next to the police station and the hilly park with the pond.

My old man's going to treat me! I'm doing all right on the baseball team and I deserve a bat. I bat seventh but make it count and on the way there we'll stop for a burger, too, at his favorite joint where they serve them big and greasy.

The sun pours into the car. The music plays on the radio, static-filled mariachi, hectic Mexican voices coming at us between the songs, exhorting us to buy sofas, cars, appliances in the greater East Los Angeles area. "*¡Compra!*" He turns it off and pats my knee. Smiles. The best, the best. My old man.

"Everything okay?"

"Everything's okay."

We sail along.

...

My old man sits erect behind the wheel of the old Falcon. *"El Falcón."*

El Falcón has been handed down to us. My mother pleaded for it. When my single aunt moved up to a sporty Mustang to keep up with her set, my mother was on the phone with her.

It was coming on.

"Please, Ellie, give us your car, so I can put away a little money for when Alberto can't work. I know it's coming on. I know it's going to be hard for a while before we get on our feet again. I'm going to have to apply for disability and..."

"...*Ay*, that's still a long ways away. Don't think about it."

"Not so long, Ellie. I can see it in his eyes. The way Estella and those relatives from his side of the family have described it. It's coming on."

"Well, sure, you can have the car, anyway, of course."

"Thank you, Ellie. That makes things easier." My mother sat at the kitchen table with a worried look. But she had a plan.

It was to save. She didn't want to splurge on the new car we needed, but in a fit of not-like-Mom extravagance, she did buy a new car two or three years up the road, bought it right before things got really horrible. She did it out of frustration and crazy anger at the Fates.

But that's the subject of another essay, that car that almost ruined us. That car that didn't help at all.

"Oh, goddamn it, I just wanted a new car! I thought if we got it God wouldn't be so cruel! I was so stupid! I thought... I was in pretend-land! Pretend-land! Damn me! Damn me! How could I be so stupid?"

Right now we're in the old Falcon, the family heap. The beloved blue junker. It groaned so much and creaked so loud around every turn you had to love it. The seats were torn and the grill was rusted and the bumper twisted and the thing roared like a beast when you started it.

But it was ours. *El Falcón.*

...

"Teach me how to cuss, Dad."

"What?" He hardly hears me.

But it's on my mind having spent an afternoon with Gilbert and his dad yesterday, Mr. Murillo, probably the king of them all.

"Fuck" was probably tattooed on his chest before tattoos became so popular.

"I think there's some kind of protest march today in East LA," my dad says.

"I don't care."

"Me neither." But on the way back from Builder's Emporium, we notice a bearded Chicano tailgating us. We hear him honking at us.

Everything goes haywire for a second. I feel scared and alone.

But then my old man saves the day. But that's not coming up for a while yet.

We haven't even gotten there.

...

It was coming on. Then it was here.

Three or four years later it bowed into our lives in a fit of forgetfulness that took him from hospital to hospital until he got diagnosed with Alzheimer's disease, the closest the doctors knew to Huntington's disease then, because my mother hid all the pertinent records documenting the incidents of the illness on his side of the family; she thought we'd be labeled nuts. The stigma was too much for her.

"Maybe it'll just go away," was the generational mantra. But it wouldn't just go away.

"It's just so horrible."

It's unbearable, not the shadow of it, but the absolute reality.

I cope with my own risk—50/50 go the odds at conception for the child of an afflicted one—with a simple plan. If I have it, if I start manifesting symptoms in the near future, I will show Jesus how to suffer. Not. I will take the gun to my mouth and blow my fucking brains out because I don't want to die like that.

"It's not dying that's frightening me," I keep telling a priest-counselor I see on occasion. "But dying like that."

"But don't you see it's all part of life. It's just another death."

"It's not just another death, Father. You don't know. I can't stand hearing about the suffering people have endured with cancer or whatever substitute they think is equal. The suicide rate for people at risk for this beast is astronomical. For a reason. It's hellish."

"It's life." He argues back, and I say my piece.

"You don't get it unless you've seen it and are at risk for the same exact thing. I won't even listen to anybody else on it. Bye!" We smile and hug because we love each other and care about each other and nothing else really matters much, does it?

"Take care."

"I will." I go out into the night fraught with anxiety.

...

A few miles up the road our stomachs growl at the same time, almost, and make us laugh. It's time to eat lunch for sure.

We stop at the burger joint and slop up the works.

"It's good, no?"

"It's good." Napkin to my mouth, wide-eyed in the fabled land East Los, always trying to figure it out. Told there're bad things here, I don't see much of it.

Then a cholo holding a sock to his nose walks in, stumbles, forces his way to the bathroom. He can barely walk.

People wince at the counter, sneaking looks.

"Don't ever do that," my dad says. "That's stupid. Poor guy. *¡Ya nos vemos!*" He yells to the cook he knows, Herminio standing behind the counter proudly in his white apron stained with food, the grill sizzling behind him.

"Okay! *¡Hasta luego!*" He waves a big hand in the air, watches the cholo, solemnly, trot outside again, his face smeared with paint.

"Jeez," he shakes his head. Goes back to wiping the counter.

...

But periods of worry come and go, and leave me unmolested for blessed chunks of time. Deep within me, I feel I don't have it. My brother, on the other hand, has it right now, as he sits in Kansas at his dining table with his wife and kids, holding hands, saying grace, a Christian.

"Amen." I've been a witness to his courage.

...

And on to Builder's Emporium we go. It's a big hardware store with a striped awning out front.

Electric doors slide open.

"You go get what you need. I'll find you."

I wander. I stand under the lights swinging a good old-fashioned #28 Louisville Slugger that I still have in my closet, leaning against the back wall.

"I want this one, Dad." I check-swing it.

"Okay, get it." He reaches for his wallet limping up the aisle, the slightly off gait better today. He's had some sleep. He's not tired.

It's his day off. The day he gets to do what he wants. The day he wants to hang around with me.

He pays with a smile. He handles this transaction, and I'm proud of him for that.

"Isn't Steve's dad a little weird?" I can hear it, unspoken, around me.

But he's not, he's not! He's okay! He's just bought a quart of oil he puts in the trunk in the parking lot.

"Get in, let's go home," he says.

I sit next to him, my bat in the back. It clatters around with the oil.

"*El Falcón!*" I shout it out.

He smiles. Smacks the cracked dashboard. "This pretty baby is all right. My baby, ha? Yours too."

...

Cases. There had been plenty, an uncle in San Bernardino, a whole family wiped out in Pacoima, cousins and nephews and both his sisters in Guanajuato, succumbing to the gene, the bad gene, symptoms and signs showing up in the fifth decade, conclusively, shadowy signs, beforehand; fifty-fifty chance: gamble, you lose. Marry a man and love your children, you lose.

...

My old man and I have made it a day. Started off from home with my mother's blessing. "Have a good time!" Turned the corner of the street in the tortured Ford and gone past the neat line of plain tract homes offering a pleasant view out the windshield. Boxy homes with small windows and, in some, larger picture windows and upgrades of one kind or another, like wrought-iron curling around a porch and manicured lawns and heavy knockers on expensive doors a little misplaced in such humble surroundings but stuck there anyway. "Rita Sanchez bought a new door! It's a nice one. Got it at Builder's on sale! Her husband installed it. He's a handyman, you know." Could do things my dad couldn't do. Calculate. Measure. Patiently hang and figure.

Especially with each passing year.

We get out of there. Ride past the park and the old convention center slated to be demolished for new homes and make a right at the busier street. Dip under the bridge to East LA.

...

My dad got sick. Turned incompetent in a night or two, a week, a month, a slow year? Who could tell anymore?

He worked for the Sante Fe Railroad, was proud of it. Was able and sturdy. Dependable. *Fuerte. Un trabajador bueno.* A good worker.

But now he was sinking fast. *Muy, muy rapido*, he was going down.

His friends from work came to tell us one night. They brought him home.

He had reached a sad point, confused at the yard. He needed to see a doctor. He was endangering other people's lives; he had lifted a heavy piece of equipment and forgotten to tell anybody and it had fallen and almost killed another worker. That's why they were here; they had been covering up for him for a long time, watching him wander around the tracks at night with a lantern in his hand, directing him and steering him away from trouble, foremen and bosses. Now they couldn't look out for him like before. He had to go.

They said this all politely and nervously, standing in our living room in their overalls, with goggles wrapped around their necks, the trainmen's kerchiefs and golden crucifixes peeking out.

Mexicanos, *con dignidad*, my father's compañeros.

My mother listened intently. When they finished, she sighed, agreed that something bad was happening. *"Algo muy, muy feo está pasando aquí."*

She thanked them for coming and bringing home her husband and offered them coffee again, whiskey, and showed them to the door kindly when they declined. In his room, my father wailed and cried; two weeks later, he was back home in bed asking, wondering, what the doctors had found out at the hospital. They had stuck a million needles in him and given him a spinal tap and he knew, staring at the ceiling in his bedroom with the small radio on, mariachi music, *puro* mariachi pouring out *("La vida no vale nada...")*, he had it. His father had it before him and he had it; trips he had taken to visit his ailing father in Tijuana stormed in his mind. *"¡Ay, es horrible!"* He cried aloud, he gasped, he wailed. He prepared us for the coming years with a symphony of misery. But this is a good memory, the good stuff!

...

East LA! A day in the capital enjoying the sights, starting with looking up under the bridge with the big Santa Fe logo painted on the metal side.

"Atchison, Topeka and the Santa Fe!" We all say when we go under it as a family, proud to be a railroad family for all the perks and lore associated with the line.

We get free passes to anywhere in the country! We make it to San Diego once a year, see the waves rolling upon the beaches, and it's enough for us; we pack a lunch. Spend a day at the zoo watching the gorillas toss shit our way... Memories!

Oh, Atchison, Topeka and the Santa Fe!

"There it is, Alberto," my mom says when we pass under it, craning her head to see the royal blue lettering circled by white. "It keeps us in tortillas."

"*Y tacos,*" my sister says, trying Spanish, and we all laugh.

She can't speak Spanish worth beans. Neither can I.
Can master the pronunciation. But beyond that, like me,
is hopeless.

Can't speak the rapid-fire stuff or understand it.

"Yup," my mother says. "There it is." Reflective, my mother is not without irony or a broader sense of the world, our own place in it amusing to her as long as things are going fairly well.

She reads, she thinks. "It keeps us, how should I say it, from needless want. They give the peasants a little more than most. Hooray, Santa Fe!" She smiles with us and enjoys the moment.

...

My old man getting sicker and sicker; meanwhile, my brother out of a job and getting in fights, trouble, because he carried the disease, had the gene, too: gamble, you lose.

My dad wild-eyed and scared, scaring my friends, not recognizing them at the door, rolling up in his wheelchair and spitting it out, "*Vaya, vaya,* shoo! Go 'way!" until he couldn't even do that.

Moaning from his bedroom, the house filled with his agony.

And my brother caught, trapped, in its snare.

It was evident from an early age. "Junior, what's wrong with Junior?" Relatives asked, out of earshot.

"Isn't he kind of like his father already, showing it?"

Friends testified to his weirdness. "Something's wrong with your brother, man. He can't act right. Is he sick or something?"

They couldn't cope with him after a time. He was too awful to be around, too mean, too moody, too unpredictable in what he might say to embarrass you, mostly, to make you feel bad and awful about yourself; not consciously mean, but stupidly oblivious to all that is hurtful. Socially unaware. Uninhibited. Unacceptable.

That was my brother. A lot like my father.

Only my father shifted to normal among adults. Courtly, kind, decent, he became a true gentleman.

Not Albert, though. He remained a pain, alone.

...

East LA! A totally familiar but mythic country a few miles away! Every trip is a journey worth recording!

Around us, the walls sound off with new graffiti.

UNITED STATES OUT OF VIETNAM! NO MORE CHICANO DEATHS! *VIVA LA LUCHA!*

CHICANO POWER! Everywhere around us.

CHICANO POWER!

East LA holds its breath, puffs up its chest and breathes out forcefully. FUCK UNCLE SAM!

BROWN BERETS ALL THE WAY!

CHICANO POWER!

East LA gains a new pride. Old-time conservatives appear in
the local paper wondering about this war now. We get news in
Commerce, down the street. Our boys are dying, too. Two in the
last year, and who knows how many since it began.

Commerce's finest. Enlistees. Draftees.

Drift above the angry signage and find a home here...

In East LA!

...

My brother wants to be a part of it; he can't. He wants to be a
cholo. My mother won't let him. "What, are you crazy?"

But he's insistent. Bussed into a bad neighborhood for junior
high, he picks it all up, the look. He wears a red headband the
day he stumbles home from a ditching party.

"Hey, homes," he greets me.

But my father moves in. He wrestles him to the ground and
takes it off at my mother's urging, "He's drunk, look at him, he's
drunk!" And his friends have ripped him off and he's bleeding
and he's drunk, hopelessly, endlessly drunk, until he's...

...

Nobody's resting these days. Everybody's rebelling.

The Protest March turned into a riot and Ruben Salazar is dead
at the hands of filthy cops, pigs, Salazar the famed journalist who
told us the truth, but the protest movement stayed alive and to

hell with the war.

"No more war! War is bullshit!"

The vets say it all, those who don't wear their medals proudly at recruitment centers. Mexican Americans always serve their country well, those fine brave soldiers known for their valor. Now they're protesting crazily, with the college kids and the peaceniks, a few of them, anyway.

I see them arguing with supporters of the war at the park, getting into it, coming to near blows a few times. "Yeah, I'm a disgrace. I'm a disgrace to the country for saying I don't like to kill people anymore, I don't believe in it. I'm going the other way." He holds a hand up with two fingers spread, looks dopey on purpose. "Peace. But it's better than this." He puts the finger in his face. "That the government gave me."

...

A Christian; sick, hopelessly, endlessly sick, in Kansas now where he just retired from the army, cheerfully, bless his soul, a Gutierrez never cries in public (a little family pride there), we lick our wounds in private; I'm breaking the family code, I'm fucking up too. I'm doing all the wrong things howling and hopping on the red hot stones of life like a gleeful idiot laughing in the face of death that ugly mask *cara de* Huntington's and doing worse even fucking and fucking with capital ABANDON heedless of consequences making love to my wife my beloved wife without a rubber the sacrament of coming partaken.

Retired prematurely because he couldn't make the grade, couldn't make it to sergeant or sergeant-plus or whatever the fuck they give you after twelve years in the service, including a stint in the air force.

So he's out, and he doesn't know it, or he knows it and doesn't care.

Doesn't let on.

I'll have a million kids with a million deformities and...

Viva the pro-abortionists! Viva the pro-lifers! Viva everything and everybody because the matter is really very simple!

"¡La vida no vale nada!" ¡Chale! I still say yes. Spread 'em, baby. Your Huntington's torpedo is coming. All I can do is laugh, and cry, and live, and go on.

All I can do is laugh and sing it again: *"¡La vida no vale nada!"* Life is worth nothing! But it's all we have.

...

We pass out of the Builder's Emporium parking lot and see it. A few protesters have snaked their way to the police station on Third Street. They thrust up signs on the sidewalk.

Are You With Us Or Not? Sign This Petition. *¡Viva La Comunidad!*

"Bring the boys home, putos!" A very angry Chicana leans out of a car and shouts to the sky. A cavalcade of bumperstickered activist-bearing vans and flatbed trucks trails her ride.

We're in the middle of it! A caravan protesting the war!

"¡Ay, caramba!" En el Falcón, the sky-blue bird good for a couple of laughs.

"Vamos a ir a Beverly Hills *en el Falcón para* trade down. I think the neighbors are jealous." A joker, my old man!

He was all right, he was all right! He was great, grand, perfect!

...

Perfectly sad. My brother's sick and my dad's dead and my mom's worried and my sister's scared and I'm mad; we're all sick of this. Rain, rain, go away, come again another day, so Daddy and Junior can play.

Motherfucker, death. *"Hay viene la muerte."* You're nothing.

An old crone told me at Olvera Street, turning over tortillas in her hands as if the figure of Death on the table before her, La Muerte, was actually making tortillas like her, cackling, laughing, *"Hay viene la muerte; mira la muerte, haciendo las tortillas, pues es nada; es nada, mijo, no llores."* That was a few months after I learned my brother was sick. I went back to Fresno where I live and prepared for another funeral, put on my best tie and jeans and sat in a church by myself, thinking of all the good things in my life, and there have been more good things than bad things, and there have been perfect days, too, days when things went well and never stopped being good.

Y La Muerte took a back seat.

...

The bearded Chicano is behind us, on our ass, a scary Chicano in a Dodge Dart ready to pierce our feathered butt, ready to bring us down. It won't take much. One little jab and we'll be dead.

He'll get off and beat the shit out of my dad. My dad can't fight!

He's not that kind of guy! He can't handle this situation!

The guy is right on our tail, feverish in his beret, scowling, giving us the finger, bearing down on his horn as he takes the turn. "GET OUT OF THE FUCKING WAY!"

Who's he so fucking mad at? We're on his side. Kind of. Were.

"Dad, that guy's honking at us! He's giving us the finger!"

"So what? We'll give him two," my dad said, and he picked up my hand and we gave him the finger. Two.

He stared at us, gape-mouthed, and floored it to catch up with the people ahead of us, already chugging away.

I held up my hand, trembling. Kept my finger frozen below the window so that people couldn't see it but I could. It was proof that my dad was all right, like everybody else in the neighborhood.

He could throw the finger when he wanted to! He could cuss with the motherfucking fathers of my friends, too, I bet! But my dad put his hand around mine and closed it.

"You don't need to show that anymore," he said. "This is a pretty day, beautiful!"

Then he hit the gas, and I swear, the Falcon soared.

At the Drive-in with My Brother

For Albert, and Norma, too, lurking in the background

My brother and I used to go to the drive-in on weekends to get out of the house. Mostly it was after a long week of washing and caring for my father, on my brother's part, doing the dirty things that needed to be done to keep him clean enough, "to keep him decent," as my mother said, "bearable." It all went past him. My father was too far gone to be aware, howling, as he was, in his room at all hours, in bed, propped up on pillows with his mouth open and pajamas wet. But my brother took care of my father as best he could, as best as his condition allowed, which was pretty dismal. He was already gone then, my father, preceding my brother into that terrible gulf of pain and irredeemable hopelessness that is my family's legacy, my family's sickly inheritance. I cursed the God that brought it to us, asshole Jesus with his minimal sufferings making me laugh when we had this motherfucker, this bastard, this son of a bitch disease, called *la cosa* in my childhood, dictating everything.

The nature of it wasn't known yet, what it was, exactly, a mystery. Trips to the hospital misnamed it. Huntington's disease, Alzheimer's disease, pre-senile dementia came flying out of doctors' mouths, got typed on to labels stuck on to folders, then printed on letters forwarded to the Railroad Retirement Board to guarantee a pension. Before he could retire, he had to be disabled. Before he was certifiably incapacitated, he had to be diagnosed. But words got thrown around. Nobody knew. Only that the chart, tracing our family's history, smudged and barely decipherable on the tree, proved a rot, a blight in our genes, in our bones.

And it was horrible.

But my brother and I used to go out on Friday nights when the mood struck us; we wanted to get out of the house. It usually proceeded from his antsiness, sprawling in front of the TV with his head on a pillow, comfortably uncomfortable, becoming fretful and disillusioned with the bad Friday night offerings.

So he would say something like, "Let's go to the drive-in, Steve."

And I would say, "Okay, dude, let's go," not really caring if we went or not, too preoccupied with my own troubles—adolescent trials scorching me in their own right—besides my own immediate grappling with *la cosa*, "the thing" in front of us, around us, all the time.

That thing was a beast, *un monstruo*, it was even said, a monster, a slayer.

This was what I gathered from the earnest whisperings between my father's cousin, Estella, and my mother years before, whisperings that took place for as long as I could remember.

"Did you know that it starts in the..."

"And how old was she when she..."

Mysterious mutterings, sudden silences when we walked into the kitchen. Kids glanced at and appraised, a lingering look at my brother. "*Ay*, kids, get out of here! Don't bother us today! Go outside and play!"

Now what we dreaded for so long appeared. Banished from our own sense of security, which was real—we were a solid enough working-class family—life itself seemed malign and at fault. Even the damn TV, zigzagging in front of us, seemed a curse.

We had to get out, especially my brother. Perhaps some elemental sense of where he was heading urged him. Maybe he knew he too was afflicted with the thing that drove us all nuts, scared us, ruined it all for us, our family life, such as it was.

And maybe his fleeing was from himself as well as my father in the bedroom. Maybe, but doubtful. I just think he wanted to get out for the night and do what was natural for him, see some near-naked women breathing heavily on the screen. He was eighteen and horny, unfulfilled at home, nearly friendless and without a girlfriend.

So I would agree to go, and then go back to whatever I was doing then, most likely nothing important—pasting Green Chip Stamps into the redeemable books, say, licking with alacrity at the table set up in the living room underneath the bloated chandelier lamp, off to the side in that small space called the dining area in the master plan of our Commerce home.

And my brother, Albert, up and active in the house now, would be gathering his stuff, keys and wallet and glasses and smokes, stopping in the hall to get a jacket if it was cold, asking me to call the Rosemead or the Gage Drive-in to find out what was playing, what we could expect when we pulled up in a little bit. Above us, off to the side behind the waving palm trees, he wanted to find the right kind of movie listed, some R-rated teaser encrypted on the milk-white billboard in stark black lettering.

I always tagged along because I didn't know what else to do. I didn't have anywhere to go or any real goals to accomplish, homework out of the question. School was a bust for me in those days, my father's screams, his head-above-bath-water frantic wailings while my brother did his best to shampoo his hair (and did it well) and tendency to whimper in the night filling my head with noises that distracted me. I had no concentrative powers, no attention span anymore. All I had was a willingness to get out, and I didn't care where.

So I would follow him out the front door to the show, as we said, to the drive-in.

"Dude, let's hit it. Let's go to the show then."

"All right."

And this night my mother was particularly beaten. She was tired, sore tired. It was in her eyes, sitting there at the end of the couch reading a novel between looking up at the TV and listening to us, half absorbed in her own world, not even raising an objection when the question of money came up, but only nodding her head absently when my brother made known his plan.

"Okay, go," she said, almost a zombie.

She even smiled weakly. She meant to keep us happy that night, obviously.

"You can go when you want." It was as if she paid my brother Albert with those trips to the drive-in, knowing she couldn't afford to give him more and that what he did for my father was beyond recompense. She loved him, loved us all, her children and husband, but hid it well, too. It didn't come out too often in those days of stress and anger. She was often irritable and moody, downright bitchy and mean, but sometimes she turned sweet and caring, generous, as when she gave my brother what he needed to save his own sanity, a night out.

She handed him the money out of her purse, which was handy on the end table next to her, reproaching him, as she did, for leaving her. "No, Albie, stay home with me, stay home tonight. It's nice here."

She pled, in a change of heart. "Please."

My father was down for the night, quiet and restful in his room, no longer making those yelping, unbearable sounds that are still in my head, and that was a moment to enjoy, to sink into, to breathe out heavily and marvel at. But the hall was dark and ominous, the pilot light flickering in the furnace, the ceiling above us shadowed and the push to go out strong.

So my brother said, "Aw, Mom, let me go," and she said sure, go.

"Okay then, go," she waved us off, settling herself on the end of the couch where she kept her vigil, watching television and listening for my dad, able, still, to muster the energy to quiet him if he woke up.

"I'll be alone here, you know," she tried one more time. But we knew she didn't mean it.

"Dad's here."

"I know," she said, emptily.

My sister couldn't comfort her this night either. She was at the drive-in herself, on a date with her boyfriend Carlos, who would later marry her. He was new in her life, but constant. He came over in a beanie to keep him warm this last month, wearing it sensibly, not cholo style, down to the eyes. It covered his ears and he blew into his hands on our porch, waiting for her. In LA, any time the breath congeals you bring out the winter wear. Heavy coats and gloves if you have them, mostly thick shirts and mid-weight jackets. It was probably in the mid-fifties when we stepped outside, but severe enough for us to remark the cold and turn on the heater in the car before starting down the driveway.

...

A short history of the genre of tits-and-ass movies might start with the V of a woman's crotch, puffed out under her bikini bottom, Samantha or Debbie or Mary Lou caught astride a hunk felled by her ferocious swing of a ball-and-chain across his face that was deadly enough to near kill him, but not without a smirk.

Tits and ass. I've seen it all. I've seen titties hanging from trees, squeezed under plumbing pipes, dancing in tune with the wind on motorcycles; seen them floating in underwater shots making sharks look tame, bouncing on top of trains threatened by fire. I've seen them all and butts, too, pouring out of denim shorts so tight they demand a license in some countries, strutting, twisting, bending, oh, yes, bending! Don't forget bending! Bending over every rail in the northern hemisphere and some south of the border, too, or on a tropical island far, far away from civilization, those cheeky effronteries to everything ordered and well managed causing havoc. I've seen them in conjunction with each other, zippers flying and buttons popping, great, mounded fleshiness hard to tell apart in the sweaty moment. I've seen proud bearers of the bounteous tits and peachiest ass escape every single predicament known to saucy womanhood and create a few, too! Torturing the warden stricken with his own insatiable need for domination and power by lustily turning the tables on him. I've seen the fertile combination stride down halls in college professor's blouse and rumpled skirt, just the wink of a nylon askew behind the leg.

And I've been bored by them. I've seen them go stale and flat, even as my brother has gotten excited, cracking up at the newest twist, leaning forward in the driver's seat at the drive-in, adjusting his glasses, asking, "Huh?"

He was a strangely unsettled guy, my brother, and unsettling, a guy you couldn't get a handle on. A complete misfit, he nevertheless hung around with what passed for hoods in our neighborhood, minor characters with no spark in them but the sarcasm and meanness of the knuckled under. He hung around with this losing set, and they called him The Goon, and the name stuck, following him everywhere he went, and he answered to it in his naiveté and kindness. "Hey! Hey, Goon, you fucking asshole! You're fucking stupid, eh!"

"All right, man, I'm The Goon!" He was terribly innocent, troubled, maddening, because he carried that beast on his shoulders. Afflicted early with the disease that was taking my father, he floundered in society. A lack of inhibition best describes him; an incapacity to understand social reserve, common relations, how we get along with each other without telling the truth or insulting one another.

And so it was hard for me to be around him, a trial for me, really. His behavior could have consequences, so un-thought out and spontaneous was it, and that was the difficult part. For instance, on a certain foggy night in town he picked up a graffiti-covered basketball from a hardcore cholo who had stumbled into our park looking for a homeboy nobody knew, and muttered, "What the fuck is this?" about that *vato's* ancient and deadly gang. And it was only with a sly and slick maneuver that I got him away from the guy before he caught on; he might have knifed him or shot him for dissing his barrio.

But he was also helpful and kind, big-hearted and good, strong. He was all of these things, and he was my brother, The Goon, Albert. Whom I prefer to call Albert.

He got me to go with him to the drive-in again for our usual pair of flicks and laughs. More came with the package: a pizza, two cokes and maybe popcorn and candy in between, my mom generous with her scant resources, always sending us off with the proviso to be good to ourselves. "Buy a large pizza, so you don't come home hungry!"

We went off in our car down our tame block, turned onto Washington Boulevard that was heavy with industrial traffic during the day, diesel trucks and bobtails inching along, but dark and shadowed now, factories looming to the side, closed for the night or emitting smoke in a bluish tint, the street empty, and lonely. We caught the gleam of liquor stores coming up, motels glowing. "*LA woman*," I whispered under my breath.

We drove on the shiny black streets into the great curving driveway, under palm trees, leading to the screen.

"All right, dude, here it is."

"Cool."

But things don't work out as easily as that. There were some difficulties that night. My brother didn't want to see the movie I wanted to see, *The Doberman Gang*. And so the motherfucker tricked me out of the house, promising my mother he was taking me to one I would enjoy, too, answering her warning with an indifferent lie.

"Not your usual smut, eh?" she shouted, enjoined us out the door, and my brother improvised with a forward grin and a hang of his shoulders, "Yeah, Mom, whatever he wants," my father waking up in his bedroom to his ongoing agony.

"Go, just go." My mother ridded herself of us.

She stood at the door, a lonesome figure. Behind her the TV sprayed radiantly and cast her in silhouette.

Then the noises started. We could hear him as we got in the car.

"Ah, ah, ah!"

"Hurry up, dude, let's go," I said. I couldn't stand those noises. Bringing them back causes a shudder.

"All right, we're out of here," my brother said.

We drove away. My brother turned on the radio, R&B that he loved, and started whistling and chuckling.

"What, man, what's so funny?"

"*The Doberman Gang,*" he said. "What?"

"Yeah, man, let's go see *The Doberman Gang,*" I said, reiterating my plan for the night. I wanted to see the movie about dogs, Dobermans, robbing a bank.

"Fuck you, dude," he said. "*Tropical Aches*, man, that's where it's at!" He laughed at me, with a sidewise look. I stared back at him.

He exploded in unbelief, pounding the dashboard, lighting a cigarette with the orange-tipped lighter, and blowing out smoke at the signal. "*The Doberman Gang*? You gotta be kidding, man. *Chichotas!* Titties! Pussy!" He pursed the ultimate thing. "That's where we're heading, man, not to your fucking dog show." In a blaze of older-than-me he had the last word.

I wanted to see that movie, too. Ever since catching the preview a few weeks before, it had intrigued me. How a pack of Dobermans could be trained to carry out a heist at a city bank was a question to be answered. Plus I liked Dobermans. The dogs were sleek and mean and arrogant. They trotted around on soft-padded paws, princes of canine society. In that rarefied world of purebreds, they stood out, part of "The Working Group," as classified by the American Kennel Club. I was into dogs then. I devoured books on them by the dozens. As many as I could get my hands on, I read and studied. Perhaps it had something to do with breeding itself and the willful refusal to accept fate as the random shot in the dark it seemed, but to find in the preordained world of a select breed something like mind and design overcoming the terror of chaos.

I just wanted to see those fucking dogs.

I sulked and even sniffled leaning against the door, staring out the window at the LA night, banging my head against the glass, softly. "Shit, man, you promised, fucker."

"Ah, man, shut up," he muttered, swinging into the big driveway that marked the Rosemead Drive-in.

We paid the lady in the booth, my brother handing her the twenty with the confident air of a working man, which he was, cigarette dangling out of his mouth, pocketing the change quickly but then deciding better and wadding it in my lap.

"Here, man, take care of it," he said, not giving a shit about money, as always. What was his was mine and what was mine was more than his, was ours.

We made our way into the drive-in; we found a spot, crunching past the other cars already parked, some fucking bad—noses up, fog lamps on, restful in the night; prize lowriders on display, and guys and girls moving into the back seats with blankets trailing after them. My brother nudged me.

He turned off the motor, adjusted the speaker in the window, settled in. I leaned back and got ready for the best-worst of it. A shadowy figure dropped down from a fence towards the back. Then another. A gang of *vatos* streamed across the asphalt toward a station wagon already weighed down with half of Rosemead, stood outside smoking.

"Let's go!" Carloads got crazy around us. Horns honked, headlights flashed on the still-gray screen, and then the scene started.

Woman walking on a beach. "Yeah!" Comes from three or four cars. Beep! Beep! Beep!

"Dude, want something to eat?" He shouted over the noise.

"Sure," I said, getting out of the car already, watching him in profile absorb the action. "What?"

"Get whatever you want," he said. "Get me a coke, a pizza. Hurry back, dude," he said. "It's started."

I came back with popcorn and cokes, saving the pizza for intermission when we would be hungriest, with one more movie to go. I set the popcorn between us and started eating, laying a bunch of napkins on the dashboard and handing him his coke. I drank mine and watched him, laboring to eat and catch the movie at the same time.

"What the fuck you looking at, dude?" he said.

"*Chichotas!*" He let out a spray of popcorn.

We started laughing, tossing popcorn across the seat at each other, cracking up and getting into the spirit of the thing, the damn movie in front of us, two broads already intertwined on the muddy hut floor, unbuttoning each other's blouses, kissing each other feverishly, entering the zone of jungle hot lust promised on the billboard.

"Nasty, eh," my brother said, and we cracked up some more, holding our mouths, not being able to contain the ridiculousness we felt watching this shit, this *cagada* with tits up on the big screen. Just another night at the drive-in with my brother. Behind us, on screen number 2, the looming shadow of a Doberman, teeth bared, appeared.

Homage to the Champ

Float like a butterfly,
Sting like a bee ...
— Drew "Bundini" Brown

I remember wondering what all the fuss was about, watching him on TV, his quick hands and loopy mouth. And I remember my grandfather and uncles discussing him, with wary faces, pondering him aloud. "Yeah, he can dance, but can he fight?"

"Vamos a ver, este Liston es cabrón."

Then I lost track of him. And now, six or seven years later, in a dry and dusty classroom, he floated into my life again and rope-a-doped me in a little-known performance four or five years before he rope-a-doped George Foreman in the most brilliant athletic spectacle of the twentieth century. But this isn't about George Foreman. This is about Ali, 1970, and a boy, widening...

"Ali! Ali! Ali!"

I finally knew what he was about that day, sitting rapt at my desk. Ding! Ding! Ali in the fifteenth chopping down Bonavena flitted across my mind, replayed itself in an endless series of variations dethroning my old hero and installing my new one.

Bonavena, the big, brawny Argentinean I had been secretly rooting for before the fight, lost his luster. Lots of things had made me in his favor.

There was the fact of Ali's race, and that weighed in. There was the fact of Bonavena's race, and that did, too. Or, rather, Ali's race didn't mean anything to me, per se, not like Bonavena's did.

But I lie. Ali's race did matter to me, deeply. But I couldn't articulate so fiercely why.

It was shameful.

All I remember was that Bonavena was my man up till then. In the Quarry fight I wanted Quarry to get smashed by Ali's fists, but in the second fight leading up to the Fight of the Century, the biggest sports event to ever take place in the history of recorded civilization, I backed Bonavena all the way. It was time for Ali to go down, drop, under that Latin American's terrible punches.

Latin American. I guess that's what I was in those days, those heady days of Ali's comeback with all the strife of the civil rights movement still alive on the streets. "Chicano Power!" echoed on my side of town.

And I wanted Bonavena to represent me in the ring, too.

Plus I remember the time a nigger—ah, there it is—jumped me and my cousin in the restroom of the Olympic Auditorium at the Wednesday night wrestling matches. There were two of them, actually, lean, brown-skinned guys pushing us up against the wall and, singling out my cousin, rifling through his pockets as he stood there sputtering with a cup of popcorn in his hand. "Motherfuckers! Motherfuckers!"

"Motherfucker yo-self, muthafucka!" And the tall one slapped him once across the face, hard. My cousin started kicking back at him, but they threw him against a wall, and things threatened to get worse before an old man, black and gentle, grandfatherly, walked in and scowled at them, saying, "Wha' the," as he made his way to the urinal unzipping his pants, one eye on them, concerned. They scrammed.

And the old man muttered something about kids nowadays, mis-behavin'.

We gathered ourselves and left. That was about three years be-fore the fight took place. We were about eight or nine then, the bloods about eleven or twelve, maybe early teens.

"Let's get out of here, Hank."

"Let's go." He was sweaty and nervous, shaken up.

So was I. I took it out on them in hate for all their kind.

"Fucking nigger." The word popped in my head whenever I saw one, a black person, which was rare. In my part of town, East Los Angeles, Mexican Americans predominated.

"Dominated," in my mind. *Latin Americans. Chicanos.* I didn't know the difference then because I was in sixth grade and full of shit myself. I hadn't stepped out of California.

But I knew it all. Latin American meant the same thing as Mexican, which meant (virtually) the same thing as Chicano (even though it didn't most of the time, in my neighborhood), which meant us. It was all worked out in my head, this Latin American lineage.

Bonavena had to win the fight, for me, for us. He had to show the world that these bad slick nigger fighters couldn't keep up with a hard-hitting Latin American containing us all, a mean hairy Italian Argentinean Chicano just like the guy next door, uh huh.

And Ali opened his mouth and upended my world. He put a stop to all this nonsense.

Where to begin? It starts in a fight and ends in a classroom. In between *Sports Illustrated* has caught the fight in photographs and words that remain with me, no matter how much I've mismanaged them, mangled them beyond belief, beyond historical credibility.

"Fuck history," I say. "I make history."

And that is Ali's legacy, too. A person from the "darker races," always looked down upon, always dismissed as second-rate and a footnote to history, rewrote the world.

My upcoming hero got into a fight, a real *pleito* with this big, hardy *vato* from Argentina named Oscar Bonavena. Bonavena was a lunk of a handsome hunk who could take a punch and give it back. Bonavena was the only man I ever seen piss Ali off. At the news conference preceding the fight, he got under his skin.

I remember him calling out to Ali sitting on the other side of Cosell at the table set up with microphones: "How come you didn't go to the army? You chicken! Here, chickie, chickie, chickie!"

Ali, scowling, couldn't brush him off. You could tell it hurt, it bothered him, it worked on his psyche the way he famously worked on others. He steamed. He showed resentment.

"Here, chickie, chickie, chickie!"

Then Oscar Bonavena came out at the bell and meant business. He softened him up.

He tore into him in time. He caught him in the ninth.

Plodding forward, he swung hard, and connected. He wobbled his legs but good. But Ali, pinned against the ropes and hurt, flashed back with old brilliance and started dancing. He gathered himself and eased Bonavena into the round-ending lesson: how not to fight a genius. Ali stood toe-to-toe with Bonavena in the middle of the ring, trading mean punches, blow-for-blow, and just when Bonavena seemed to have the edge, Ali tricked him with a magnificent flurry of lefts and rights coming at him from all angles, backpedaling again out of harm's way.

The ninth round, the killer round Ali survived after taking it hard on the chin only steeled him. He came out for the next one, refreshed. Bonavena met him again, and wished he hadn't. He did his best, tiring. Ali saved his best for the last.

"Here, chickie, chickie, chickie!" registered in his mind with annoyance, not anger.

What to do about an idiot like Oscar? End him.

Knock him out. So he did.

Ali set him up, crushed him in the fifteenth with an exquisite punch sent from heaven. Just a perfect left hook on the chin, or was it a clarifying crisp right cross that dropped that brawny

Argentinean to his knees, and propelled him onto his back in a
slow roll, Oscar staring up at the lights for the third time that night?

I don't know what it was, rightly. But I remember turning the
pages, seeing the man, arms flung up high, high, high, dancing
to the rafters almost, on tiptoes, jiggling, proclaiming, "I am the
greatest, I am back," after a grueling, tough fight with a top fight-
er, a ranked contender, a bad hombre, indeed.

And I remember thinking, "Man, this guy's too much," feeling
the thrill of his arrogance and gentleness coming together at the
same time. I had seen him on TV enough times to recognize a
good soul when I saw one.

I flipped the pages and laughed; there was something about the guy.

Sweaty in the corner after the fight with a towel to his face,
"Bring me Joe Frazier, bring me Joe Frazier!"

And poor Oscar Bonavena on his knees, groping for his mouthpiece.

And the capper, the punch line, doesn't even take place in a
ring. It occurs before the fight, long before the fight with the
Argentinean materializes. It happens in a stuffy locker room after
Ali has dressed, worked out, changed, sweated, danced...

He is walking around in a funk because of some bad news Drew
"Bundini" Brown has given him. Drew "Bundini" Brown the shaman,
the priest-man, the immortal versifier, deserves a special nod too.

"Float like a butterfly, sting like a bee! Rumble, young man,
rumble!" The anointed one's visionary guru mutters poetry and
speaks of God, God, God constantly. His union with Ali is holy.
It is based on the simple belief that Ali is special, that in him the
human race will find some succor. Poet, charmer, conman, loyal
help, Drew "Bundini" Brown stayed with him till the end, dying
in an SRO in Los Angeles long after the glory had faded, the best
years gone, still asking the fundamental questions: "I want to
know if God is. I want to know why we here. The grass be green
outside and I be blue inside. Why?" Poet sitting in a straight-

backed chair by a window overlooking a skid row alley kept composing.

Now it is after the Quarry fight when Ali is flush with victory. On the road to conquest, to reclaiming what is his—a belt, the title Heavyweight Champion of the World—Ali is impatient. So are others.

Oscar Bonavena, the mad Argentinean, is after Ali's ass, wants him bad, too, almost as much as Ali wants Frazier. And Drew "Bundini" Brown thinks aloud, dares to question him, restrain him, not believe in him, coming out with a cautionary note, concerning even Bonavena. "Maybe, maybe, we should wait a little more, Champ, before we go after that one."

And Ali, incredulous, wide-eyed, gaping, shoots back. "Drew, I thought you knew me? Git a contract out on him! *Git that Spanish fool in the rang!*"

And I started laughing. I started laughing right there at my desk.

Drew "Bundini" Brown can't hold him back! Nobody can!

"Champ, Champ..."

"Didn't you hear me? Didn't you? You deaf or something? *Git that Spanish fool in the rang!*"

And my shoulders shook, and my eyes moistened.

"Stephen, what is the problem there?"

"Nothing, Mrs. Rivera, nothing." I got up to sharpen a pencil and returned.

I unfolded the magazine in my desk, carefully, against the teacher's threats.

"Be serious now, for the last half hour."

And I fell seriously in love.

I learned more about him but really knew everything I needed to know already. Grandness, confidence, humor and courage defined him.

It was all there on the page.

"Ali! Ali! Ali!"

A song in my ears, a fire in my heart.

A triumphal cry sounding all around me, singing, "Ali! Ali! Ali!"

I saw him in my mind's eye approaching the ring after a three-year layoff ready to bang, wiping his feet on the rosin and bouncing in the corner, loosely and confidently expecting that he can handle the worst to come. "I am just so good. I am without worries. Allah is with me."

He carried the truth into the ring. He was God's holy warrior.

Every time he walked down the aisle he showed it, this luminescence radiating off him like the myriad sweat droplets flying from an opponent's head when he punched him.

Singing, "Ali! Ali! Ali!"

And he thrilled the world. He looked so damn good fighting, so graceful, he gave new meaning to the words "the sweet science." He was, and is, the preeminent ballet master of the twentieth century.

You can't count the Russians when you have Sonny Liston playing opposite you.

Singing, "Ali! Ali! Ali!"

And he gave more than he knew. He broke the rules of who should speak up and be heard. In a racist age with a clear hierarchy of being, whites at the top and blacks at the bottom and browns somewhere in between, but with nobody, nobody reaching the holy plateaus of whiteness, of what it means to be white in America, let alone the world, except bona fide whites and real whites alone, he resisted, drawing on his own natural strength. He simply presented himself as he was, never second-guessing his first-class citizenship nor questioning his innate superiority, and transmitting his belief so forcefully he compelled an audience.

You had to listen, even if you hated the loudmouth. Then you realized anything derogatory aimed toward him would slide off him. And that was the final blow, the sneak punch that dropped you unexpectedly because your world had been overturned. In a small but real way things didn't operate like they used to when the old putdowns didn't work anymore, when they had no real meaning for a man as big as him.

Singing, "Ali! Ali! Ali!"

Big. Strong. Quick. Fun-loving. Serious. Foolish. Tragic. Great.

"I am a man, first, beholden to nobody and limited by no rules except my own," is what his legacy is really about.

All that screaming and shouting and flailing comes down to this:

"The word *nigger* rolls off my skin. Nobody can define me except me, and God, and you, if you love me, and only if you love me."

So, too, the word *wetback* means nothing to me.

I am bigger than any reduction you may use to keep me in place. I am over you now.

Your biggest weapons are toys in the self-love I show every day.

Singing, "Ali! Ali! Ali!" all around the world, swelling so fully.

And I cried one year later when he lost to Joe Frazier in the Fight of the Century, shed bitter, anguished tears against my bedpost, wailing, "He lost, he lost," to the deep chagrin and incomprehension of my parents standing over me with worried faces.

"*¿Qué está pasando?*"

"Ali lost."

"So, he'll be back."

How right they were.

You couldn't keep him down. He was meant to rise, rise, rise.

And he did, transcended everything meant to keep him down. Kentucky and the US Army and Christianity and time and old age, too.

Transcended them beautifully, spectacularly, movingly.

Bodily.

Moving across the ring with mastery the angels took notes on.

Bam! Bam! Bam! Letting the fists fly without breaking a step in the graceful dance.

And fell, too. In the later days he suffered the cosmic wrath because he sinned against the gods, early on. You can't go sinning against the gods early on or later on or at any time in your life. You just can't.

And that's what Ali did. But he accepted his comeuppance like the man he was, never complained a word about it or begrudged nobody nothing.

And that is where his true greatness resides.

It comes with his bowing down to fate. It comes with his total acceptance of his sentence.

It was foreordained. As far back as the Fight of the Century he uttered the words that doomed him in the eyes of the gods.

The claim reached their ears, and a decision was made in council. "He is an errant child. He has sinned against us. Take note of it forthwith, and when the time comes to act, strike him down. Meanwhile, watch him with delight. He is fun, isn't he? I love him for all he offers in the way of human confidence," spoke the eminent personage presiding over the session.

And Ali felt a shiver in his back, and he smiled and shrugged down on earth. Got back to work for his last great performance.

Singing, "Ali! Ali! Ali!"

He gave the press conferences a spin that was downright ugly and undeserving of a "spokesman for the race." But heroes and prophets are never perfect.

"There's gonna be a thrilla, in Manila, when I get the gorilla!"

He set the seal of his own doom with the fury he inspired in his great nemesis, Joe Frazier, the beating he suffered in that fight largely regarded as the cause of his pugilistic dementia that complements his Parkinson's.

"Wait until I get the gorilla in Manila, what a thrilla!"

And he beat the rubber gorilla he held in his hand, and he called Joe nigger. Again and again he called Joe nigger. If not by that word exactly, he said the same thing anyway with his hand-held gorilla pointed at the audience of media hounds, laughing away.

"There's gonna be a thrilla, in Manila, when I get the gorilla!"

And Joe Frazier grinning at the mike with a little secret for Ali: "I got something for you, baby."

Came a time when the talk ended, and the fight started. Here came Joe, smokin' like an Olympic-bound twenty-year-old, with all his powers back. For fourteen rounds, he burned a path to the man who called him bad, bad things, winging up and at him as fiercely as he could. He didn't relent, banging the head, the body, the head, the body, and Ali gamely with him.

"Come on now, Joe, you can do better than that. You're fighting God!" Undisguised, he revealed himself.

"I'm God, Joe, I'm God!"

Just like me, God.

I'll pay my dues.

The story picks up.

All confused I reiterate my first findings. Something changed in me that day. I quit hating black people on sight or on principle or in any way. I expunged the "n" word from my consciousness with deliberate effort, though to do so entirely is almost impossible in our current civilization.

I danced in my chair at my desk. I moved with a shoulder-bobbing weave, smiled widely. I gulped away all shame and fears, remembering the humiliation of the mugging, and the uneasiness of feeling hate. I put it aside. I sat in the classroom and affirmed, glowed, came on to something bigger than us both, bigger than us all, knocked-kneed with that spread of Ali on my lap.

Singing, "Ali! Ali! Ali!"

All right. It goes on.

It never stops.

The Spot

There in our city, not too far from our houses and the park and
the whole conglomeration of city hall and library and post office,
sat a squat building with drab gray walls and dark windows at the
very top. Headquarters for an electronics firm, it employed many
people and saw them go home at night. They drove down the
long ramp to the street below in a slow line with their fog lamps
on, escaping the parking lot with quick turns and jets of speed.
Then it was empty and quiet up there. All the kids knew that to
be true because we trekked up the same long ramp either alone
(how brave of us! We bragged about it later and made up stories
of kidnappers in capes coming after us with wicked smiles on
their faces) or went up in raucous groups to check out the view
and mess around on the asphalt. We ran around playing tag and
riding bikes when we were younger and then changed our game
when we were older.

We went up there to make out with girls in The Spot. The Spot
was a tightly wedged corner by a buzzing electrical storage shed
that overlooked the city, a metal structure vibrating your back
when you stood against it. The parking lot stretched out in all directions; it was wide, black pavement marked with yellow lines.

And I held my first ass there, cupping that handful of delicious
flesh, and almost got a hickey I pulled away from scared and
laughed nervously about. I dug my face in the collar of my heart-
throb's pea coat as I grabbed another handful of ass and told her,
"Not now."

We kissed for hours.

The moon was up.

Across the street the library was letting people out; groups of
two or three kids came out the front door and got lost behind the
trees that hid the pathway from sight.

My city spread out before me spectacularly, all the distant indus-
try active under lighting seen from afar. Closer to The Spot, my

neighborhood throve. Porch lights signaled life in houses that were small and cozy, with cars pulling up into driveways with warm, red taillights on.

I liked my neighborhood, Rosewood.

The bank shone blocks away, a stolid wall of windows lit up sporadically fifteen stories high.

We kissed all night until she had to go home.

"I have to go home now."

"Do you really?"

"Yeah."

"Okay, I'll walk you home."

"You better!"

"We can stay for a while, huh?"

"Just a while."

We looked into each other's eyes, and smiled.

"What's your sign?"

"Leo, the lion."

"Of course."

"Yours?"

"For me to know, you to find out."

"How?"

"Like this."

We made it last. Her name was Julia and I was in love with her as much as I've been in love with anybody in my life, it occurs to me now. And after we broke off, parted lips that were wet and moist with saliva, I walked her home to the corner at the far end of the block.

"Bye."

"Bye." She gave me a quick peck on my cheek and hurried home with her arms crossed under her breasts.

I watched her go away and then went to the park, fast, where the court lights were still on and would be for a couple more minutes, and played a quick game of basketball with my friends, frantic and fresh.

"What's wrong with you, Steve?"

"Nothing, man. I feel great."

We ended the game and sat on the bench a long time in the night, talking in the dark. I couldn't tell them what was on my mind but I could explain, rapidly, what was wrong with the world. There wasn't enough light; curfew came too soon.

They agreed and nodded their heads. We walked across the park, bouncing a basketball against the sidewalk. Great echoes re-verberated off the handball courts. We wondered how long they would last, counting the seconds.

"No way."

"Let's see."

"One..." Following the path with the basketball our guide, we curved our way home under the moon, the gorgeous moon hanging above us, and made small bets, reconsidered.

"No, no..."

"Where were you at tonight, dude?"

"You wish you knew, ha? I was at the library first..."

"Shut up, they're dying."

We argued the last stretch, straining to hear. We couldn't catch it anymore, the faint echoes sounding in the night, the loud hollow booms diminishing to a muffled vibrato, an airy remnant.

STEPHEN D. GUTIERREZ

Part Three

The River in My City

The river in my city is a mean river, a stingy river hesitant to give any lifesaving waters when you need them. When you desire all that the river has to offer, crave its life-affirming qualities with a desperate yearning, the river holds back, asks "More, more, more!" from you than you want to give. It wants all, so you turn away in disgust and fear, dejected and sad.

This is the awful truth. The river is no plaything but an ugly force.

I would like to take a moment, then, to describe the river.

The river runs through my city, the City of Commerce in LA, and makes itself felt day and night with its turbulent roar. It runs behind the houses on Bartmus Street, just a regular river to the outside viewer but full of enchantment to us, the denizens of this small, tidy neighborhood not known for its natural wonders but indeed marked by its presence.

"Roar, roar, roar," goes the river all night, and when you stand aghast at its power it pays no attention to you but just keeps on going.

So it has always been, so it is.

...

So it was then.

"Stay away from the river, it's dangerous!" they warned us as kids, those good people our parents guiding us well. "Don't climb that damn ivy hill so you can watch the trucks pass! You're going to get killed!"

They knew little about the barges that, entering the river, floated unsteadily side to side before straightening up and, the captain catching sight of us, saluting us with a crazily appropriate toot, a fog-cutting blast.

"You've got no business up there!" they said. But that was long ago.

Now we watched the river from afar. On an island within view of it, we gauged its mystery. There, in a hut marked Recreation Hall, I played ping-pong with my friends, or past the brambles encircling the island, smoked pot with these same jokers in a clearing or, finding a secluded spot to puff on a joint after the elemental warning, caution, approval and recommendation all rolled up in one (ha ha!), "This is some really good shit, man, check it out!" I enjoyed the slow burn alone, without company, and later joined them. We walked across the fields in adolescent funk or pleasantly high. With my friends, I explored what I already knew so well.

We gathered early at a safe spot and commenced our routine with little formality. "Hey, dude."

"Hey, dude."

From our vantage point, the river could barely be seen on the other side of the island. We needed to stand on a table, climb a tree, squint hard and bring it into focus, into fleeting sight, the river. But weren't we too old for that? Yes, we were, so we pretended silliness, and took ribbing as the price. "What are you doing up in that fucking tree?"

"Nothing. Getting all cosmic."

"I got your cosmic. Get down from there before I haul your ass down, you monkey dick." But when I caught sight of it, I didn't care what the fools thought of me.

"It's cool, man."

"What?"

"The river."

"What the fuck you talking about?"

"The river in our city." It roared and it bubbled. Even from far away, I could sense its power and frothy surge, its white-streaked flow and reddened backwash.

"You guys ought to check it out, it's real."

And so on the island we passed our time, and lived, and grew older, and laughed, and shared secrets escaping our hearts with a little too much booze washing down whatever grief we swallowed hard and tried to forget.

...

We all came from spots that marked us in different ways, nobody knowing the extent of those markings till later, sometimes not even the nature of them. So Ray's dad, who we always thought Native American because of the ruddiness of his face, turned out to drink hard. Dennis' mom, so nice and generous, nursed a deeper problem of bitterness and hate. Unemployment plagued a family because of sloth and no other reason. Not because of the goddamned economy and the fucking Japs taking over, as Mr. Jimenez claimed, burping, every time you bumped into him in his garage, sitting on a high stool, nursing a tall one at the work bench littered with empties.

A cheap radio tinned out dispiriting *rancheras*. "You boys get the hell out of here, okay? I'm thinking."

He was thinking. Everybody was thinking.

But the river went on its way without a care in the world, as my mother might say. It did its work.

She was tied down on the bank, struggling, gasping, at the first sign of flooding. She was unbearably soaked.

She was a sad strange creature beset by problems, she was, with deep-brown, penetrating eyes full of intelligence and hurt, and sternness setting her lips in desperate survival mode during these years that I am talking about here.

She kept a watch over me.

"Are you going to the park?"

"I am!"

"Come home early! Dad needs you!"

"For what?"

"Just come home early! You live at the damn place!"

"Better than here!"

"Get out! Get out of my hair!" She screamed out the last word.

She set me loose and free, propelled me out the door. Into the night I went. It was my special time to be, and live, the night.

I walked on solemnly.

"Okay, so I'm going now. I won't tell anybody you're a witch," I muttered to myself. But I didn't mean it.

I didn't mean it at all. It was just the thing to say.

Everybody bore a burden. Everybody kept a secret or two, tucked safely away in a pocket he didn't know disallowed complete concealment, like a soiled handkerchief sticking out of a breast pocket unbeknown to the wearer strutting about so confidently.

But no matter! These personal histories marking us so definitely, these incomprehensible trials stamping us early and terribly without our knowing it didn't consume us yet. They could be left behind at the island, with the river's help. We didn't know, though, that the river was bringing us more troubles even as it washed away our old ones.

We didn't know, we didn't know. How could we know?

We were mere babes in—excuse the phrase—the woods. At the island!

And the woods were dark and mysterious and haunting, but without terror yet, because we had each other, clinging fast, no matter how coolly we played it off. No matter how ignorant we chose to be.

"Hey, Steve, how's it going?"

"Great! How about you?"

"Great!"

Most of the time, I'm saying, this is the way it went. This is the tone we set.

And then we got into it, lost ourselves, and became kids again. We gamboled on the island till the sheltering lights dimmed, one by one, and we, traipsing along still or sitting in the bleachers of the baseball field impressing ourselves with grand tales now or caught in a game of basketball at the other end by the railroad tracks so rusty and defunct they led to nowhere, remarked the sudden darkness and got ready to leave.

"Let's split, man."

"All right."

When we gathered up to go home the river was cold and uninviting. Crossing the shallow tributaries that fed it, we knew death in the air. Around the banks of the waterways, animals scurried in the bushes and night turned still.

It was lonely walking home, parting at the water's edge.

"Okay, man, see you later!"

"Okay."

"How's your dad, man?" somebody might ask, a final parting.

"He's okay, man."

The friend might pause for me, but, getting nothing, go on.

And so we split up, each of us taking his separate trail, sometimes accompanying one another as far as a lighted shack, a glowing cabin in the night. Then we said goodbye.

"See you later, man."

"Later."

And we went into our homes.

In our homes whatever was happening was news to us.

...

So the river reached into our lives regardless of any wall meant to keep it out. It was too powerful and mighty to be contained. Part of a vast system of tributaries and creeks, smaller rivers and assorted waterways, it was, one way or another, The River, all of it.

It defined our small city by its presence. "The Santa Ana. The 5." It was so important a river, so vital a waterway it couldn't be avoided as a landmark worthy of recognition. It was a concrete signature spelling us out for the rest of the city around us, the one we also belonged to, LA. It put us on the map of the nation, of the world!

The river runs right through Commerce! It traffics in commerce through Commerce! Big, grinding, roaring barges keep it busy all day! It surges with the day's traffic!

It's kind of dangerous, too, so loud and noisy and grim.

But to hear the river at night was a joy. Under cover of darkness, wide-eyed, alone in bed with an old rag dog retrieved from the garage recently, I tuned in, and, unashamed now in my solitude, in my room, opened myself to everything comforting without fear of ridicule. Rules against acting like a kid didn't apply anymore.

Gruffy the Puppy whispered things to me. "Listen to the river," he said. "Listen, and don't be afraid."

The river roared, a constant rush, an edifying current, a drowning-out solace.

"Listen to the river," he said. "Sink into it and die."

Then I turned to my brother in his bed.

"Albert."

"What?"

"Are you awake?"

"Yeah."

"What's wrong with Dad?"

"He's getting worse."

"At least he's quiet tonight."

"Yeah."

We paused in the night.

"Go to sleep, dude. It's late."

...

One night, coming home from the island, I encountered chaos. The river had overflowed its embankment and wanted to drown everything. Flooding the house, the river had soaked carpets, walls, knocked over furniture bobbing in a topsy-turvy dance in the kitchen.

"What happened?" I asked.

"Nothing. Mom hit Dad. Get in the car," my sister said.

Then the keys were thrust into my hand.

On the way out I saw my father sunk into his wheelchair, ankles wet, sulking with the glowering rage of the trapped. His arm was bruised with a purple blot and his face was scratched along one cheek.

I splashed through the living room and out the front door.

In the driveway, my mother was ready. She stood timorously alert by the car. As if the river had bested her, she looked frenzied and beaten, frazzled and alive. She clung to a small life preserver, pressing it to her chest unawares.

"Mom, let's go."

I eased her into the car and got in after my sister took her place behind the driver's seat. I drove along the main tributary getting us out of our city. From a certain point, I could loop onto the river beneath it.

It flowed beneath a bridge, constantly sparkling, constantly inviting. In my river-ready barge, I could take her away. We could escape the inferno of the house, free ourselves from the upended, dismal mess back there, the hot-breathed locus of the river's boiling heart.

It wanted us now, inside her. It wanted us for some time now.

"Come, come, come to me," it sang.

My father's slide into the river's maw cost us terribly. What he suffered from, only the river knew for sure. In those days, such obviously damning, never-heard-before words made little sense.

"Early Alzheimer's." "Huntington's." "Mid-life dementia."

Whatever it was, it robbed the mind, prematurely, awfully.

Whatever it was, it hurt.

Now my mother sat next to me, stone-faced and fervent, her eyes alive, her hands tightly clenched in her lap.

"Where are we going?" she asked.

"I don't know. Where do you want to go?"

"Grandma's," she said. "Take me to my mother's."

"Okay."

So that would mean another route. But already we had reached the apex of the bridge's arch. Below us the river roared, the car stopped at a red light. Outside the windows the cascade of shiny white droplets streaming in one direction curved against the cascade of shiny red droplets streaming in the other, all of it attended by the roar, the roar of the river.

My mom made a quick move. "Mom!" I jammed the car into park and followed her out.

On the bridge overlooking the river flowing beneath us, a gleaming, broad expanse of turbulence and beauty, I caught her. She had reached the rail and was throwing herself over, one leg—who could imagine such strength in her?—lifted high and her body aimed in the opposite direction, down below, directly at the river. She presented herself to it, and it said, "Yes, yes, jump, jump!"

I pulled her back with force. I got her in the car.

My sister got in on the other side of her, trapping her between us, and we drove away, away, away from the river behind us, its terrible beauty still a mystery.

Fragments
From a busted intro

I was walking down the street in Berkeley one day after a session with my shrink. I was on the famous Telegraph Avenue that was full of street people and Saturday vendors. Blankets lay on the sidewalks and advertised jewelry. More formal booths tilted on the street near the curb.

I kept on walking with no real plan. When I got to Cody's and saw that it was going out of business, the venerated bookstore falling prey to the indifference that attended literary culture, I stopped in front of its doors.

I looked inside and saw the cashiers pounding away with a long line of people stretching into the store. "Takes a dying bookstore to sell books," I remarked to myself.

Turning around, I saw a sales bin with two guys standing around it. I joined them.

The bigger guy reached a hairy hand into the bin and pulled out *Elements*, a collection of stories and essays by a fabulous writer.

"Chicano dude," he said, "who sold out." He passed it on.

"Yeah, I heard about him," the smaller guy said. "Such a waste. He had something going but blew it." He stuffed the book into his pants.

"I'll sell this at the flea market and make some change."

"I'll buy it for a quarter," his partner said. "If you'll split the profit."

"I'll be lucky to get a nickel for it."

The smaller of the two, a white guy, wore an intellectual's wire-rimmed glasses and a dirty white tee shirt advocating REVOLUTION. The bulky Chicano wore brown work pants and a yellow tee shirt that said nothing. NOTHING.

He pulled out another book from the bin. *Live from Fresno y Los* got waved at his friend.

He stuck that one in his pants, too.

"Hey, you can't do that!" I yelled. "You owe me royalties!"

But then they started talking about literature in the abstract, and they convinced me that it was only a punk who accepted money for words. "Like, don't be that way, man," the Chicano said.

The white guy nodded his head sagely.

"Hey, let me ask you something," he said. "Before you go."

"What? Go ahead."

"What'd your old man die of? I'm kind of confused."

"A lot of people ask me that. You must know my stuff a little bit?" I asked, hopefully.

"Yeah, a little bit," the white guy admitted.

The Chicano grunted next to him. They were fast becoming true amigos.

"Well, all right, I'll tell you. My old man died of early-onset Alzheimer's with complications. When I wrote earlier work that appeared in *Elements* and my latest addition to *My 3-Volume BOXED Set, The Mexican Man in His Backyard,* I didn't know that. It wasn't until later that they nailed it with my brother's death, slicing him open and all that, dissecting his brain. But when my dad suffered the disease, it was Huntington's. They didn't have the knowledge yet. You *vatos* want something to eat?"

"All right. We'll talk about literature."

"Nah, fuck that. We'll talk about anything but. It's Saturday in Berkeley, the sun is shining."

"*Simón*," the Chicano said.

"All right," the white dude said.

We began walking up the street, together.

...

The Ferris wheel spun and spun at the Big Fresno Fair, and nothing else mattered.

...

The Mexican man kept his back to the world. All he wanted was peace.

He watched TV under the looming trees in his backyard. A few years before an ambulance hauled him away in the middle of the night, he knew the harmony of the cosmos.

His wife stood on the sidewalk fingering a rosary as he got lifted into the last vehicle he would ride in, wrapped in a sheet. His Dodgers cap stuck out the top. She insisted on that touch.

The moon hung heavily in the sky.

...

And Ernesto Trejo knew certain things about me that I didn't know myself. He knew that I had something to contribute in the area of letters, even though I was a fuckup known for drinking too much beer around town.

He knew what the angels in our lives know. "You are something, Steve. Be it."

I dropped to his feet and kissed them.

...

And Death haunted my life. It was there the whole time. It was everywhere. It was in Herrera's eyes, and it was on the breath of the Greeks. It was in my weed-reeking clothes, overlaying it, and at home, it was in every corner of the house, waiting. Because it was surely, most certainly, absolutely without a doubt in my dad's eyes dogging me that whole time with their questioning agony.

"*¿Por qué, por qué?*" he asked, and Death laughed. He threw his head back and answered.

"What do you want me to say?"

When we had nothing to say in return, when our own voices failed us and we stood speechless but satisfied with Death, not at all upset at his doings, only then did he pack up his bags and, shrugging his shoulders as if the whole thing had been a mistake, leave the room.

...

La Muerte made tortillas all day, tossing them on to the *comal* behind the old lady on Olvera Street, laughing, cackling away, calling out on the cobblestoned street. "*¡Tortillas! ¡Tortillas! ¡Compren sus tortillas!*" People rolled them with butter and ate them happily.

It was the best kind of snack for tourists who had tried everything else.

...

Close to my house, a factory guarded its property with Dobermans. Every night, trained guard dogs roamed the grounds after being let out of cages in trucks stamped with the company name. K-9 SECURITY. It was a very tricky business, the handler releasing the un-muzzled dogs with sharp commands that woke them up. Kneeling by them, gripping the collars, filling a narrow entrance with chain link around them, he let them go, one by one, into the parking lot. They sped off over the asphalt, scooted under the trailers parked against the wall, came out again snarling and thrashing against the fence, the handler already locking the gate. They yapped, with sharply curved teeth biting at the air. Saliva traces whipped around their heads. Under the moonlight, my friends and I stared at them when we did a factory cruise on our bikes out of boredom.

They stared back, growling, pacing, sniffing under the fence at our shoes. With sudden force, lifting off from the ground like a rocket, showing his mottled belly and sharp claws, looking down at us with yellow eyes and bared teeth as he cleared the barbed wire, the head Dobie shot straight up one night and hung in the air for a preternatural second.

"Fuck! Run!" We turned on our heels and ran, leaving our bikes behind on their sides until we had the courage to come back, dogs safely away.

"Man, that was scary."

"Yeah, it was, man. You never know what's coming next."

...

"Watch him lean against the ropes, son. He's taking it. He knows what he's doing, though. Look at the sharpness of his punches coming off the ropes. Damn! That's a master at work. The old man is taking apart the young hothead. He doesn't have a chance."

My son and I watch the greatest fight ever, the Rumble in the Jungle. I don't think there is a stronger testament to the human spirit in the twentieth century than this magnificent piece of performance art enacted on the canvas in Zaire that sweaty night in 1974. I think it will last in the archives of human endeavor as long as art is valued. Make no mistake.

I am not stretching my definition. It has to be considered about as perfect a piece of *art* we have. It is an unerring, gutsy execution of a near-impossible task honoring spirit and balance and intellect and fortitude, the body at work as the mind calculates and reacts. Destroys. Creates in the next instant a new opportunity for itself.

It is brilliant. It is genius.

"Jesus, he's going down! George Foreman is going down!"

"How did he do that?"

"You saw it. With style. With everything he knew thrown in there, and just a little more. My God," it makes me weep every time. "My God."

...

It's too sad, too sad, Julia, falling apart under her father's molestation, and, walking the streets again, remembering, maybe, The Spot.

...

And the river in my city washes me ashore. I lie among the bracken, scattered about.

"There he is, in pieces," you say. You poke at me with a stick.

You nudge me together.

"He's still breathing. Let's see if he gets up and walks."

And I rise.

The World Came Crashing Down On My Wife; or, Goodnight, Señorita, Home Again, Being An Exploration Of Certain Intense Emotions Having To Do With Me And My Wife, Culled From An Old Story That Went Bankrupt And Went Like This, Something Like This; Experimental Jive, Horseshit, Mishmash, All Right?*

The world came crashing down on my wife. She had had her warning. In graduate school, a snooty institution in the east where I had fucked up in the famed writing program and she had excelled in the narrow field of her choice, her professors had warned her. In dry, subtle tones they told her that maybe this great state university in the west wasn't the place for her. Couldn't she wait for something better, hang on just another year to see what came up, hmm? "It might be just the way to go, Jacqueline."

One professor said frankly: "I wouldn't go there for all the money in the world. You're making a grave career mistake." God was guiding her all the time.

He didn't let her down. He leaned back in his chair and smiled at her, not God, but the professor in his office.

"Think about it."

She stood her ground in the doorway. "I want to go out west. My boyfriend belongs there, in the west. We're going to get married and

---

*She cracked up, real bad, spending two weeks in the Fresno hospital under the care of a shrink who kept saying her father molested her, which wasn't true. God molested her, prodded her, poked her awake. He forced her into confessing her need for him. In the Fresno hospital, on her knees, she swore off the bottle, pride, all bad things, and buried her head in the pillow and cried. I was there, touching her shoulder. The whole phalanx of soldiers who had attacked her from behind, a great woman, faded into the sunset out the window.

The sun blazed bright and orange, meaner than ever. It filled the room with scary light. Why? I don't know. But I do know that sorrow and shame were in that room; that a lifetime of mercy shown to other people came to her, despite her arrogance and blindness, too, in dealing with others.

The presence we call God reached a big hand down and placed it on her shoulder.

"Don't leave me, Stephen," she said. "Don't leave me."

"Leave you," I said. "I just got here." And we both cried a little.

make a life for ourselves. Maybe even," she blushed, "have a baby."

"Jacqueline, I'm happy for you." He relented, like all of them. "Best of luck!"

"Yes, we'll need it!"

I was doing poorly. The light grew dimmer around her head, then brighter. She drank, tipped a glass to her lips every night after school when she sat in front of the TV, zoned out.

I washed the dishes.

"But the east will be opened up for you soon," they said.

She drained her glass and put it in the sink.

So we pulled up stakes, packed up, hit the trail, WESTWARD BOUND, *señor* Gutierrez *el primer* pioneer holding the reins to the covered wagon as we ventured over the unfamiliar terrain. She ordered a cold beer in a small town, beaded and with a colorful cap that she played with on the checkered tablecloth as we waited for our food.

The horses neighed outside. I hitched up my overalls and checked under the wagon wheels for axle rot before we took off again. Didn't find any, but greased the ball bearings with her smile anyway, climbed aboard and yelled, "Giddyap!"

The horses took off, snorting and galloping. God smiled, the clouds parted, and a shaft of sunlight...

Followed us to Fresno where I signed on at the local livery and got me a job, yup, that's what I did. I rolled up my sleeves and...

Bullshitted no more with my life, doing a little this, a little that...

To get by and pull the pieces together of that unfinished mess that was grad school.

Meanwhile, things didn't stop, no, not for a second, on her side. She prettied herself up in the finest calico and owned my body on wild weekends working out the despair. The despair was real.[1] The English Department was not.

She chronicled her doings in impassioned letters to her old professors at the snooty institution back east, these gentlemanly fellows teaching two classes a term (if that), and reclining in comfortable offices with ivy clinging to the windows. They worked hard at their scholarship, and deserved it, this ideal set-up. I say this in case you think I harbor populist sentiments against behemoth institutions supporting fine minds.

I don't.

Aquí no mas estoy en la lucha.

I'm just here in the fucking struggle.

But she railed and ranted, all right. She wrote them often.

"I'm miserable, the savages are not noble. They are mean and petty, everybody wants to publish publish but they don't have anything to say. In the meantime, department politics consumes me, I'm in it, in the thick of it, it's awful but rewarding in its own unsatisfactory way. God, I'm beginning to sound like an academic out of hell. It's shit, complete bullshit, but necessary when you have a bunch of conservative hicks masquerading as liberals pushing their anti-affirmative action plans down our (my! the wild bad woman's!) throat here in the valley where you have a 50 percent Chicano population bewildered and confused at school, half of them at least, because they don't have any role models to attend to. Like an Asian-American colleague said in a fervent pitch to hire another scholar in his field, another (gasp!) Asian-American professor (he's retiring and afraid nobody will offer his courses anymore): 'My Hmong students tell me things that they don't tell you.' Don't they see the need for more diversity on campus, that it isn't just a catchall phrase but a firm commitment to make this place real? To make this place real, *real*, REAL? Oh, god, I'm dying! I'm feeling lousy, my research languishing, everything slipping out of my grasp now. I'm sinking, drowning in a sea of torpor." She didn't send the letter but filed it away with many other miscellaneous pieces of writing that ended up nowhere: articles, commentaries, conference papers, even some poetry that showed sparks of...

She was on a roll...

I was just glad to be back in the west where I belonged. I didn't belong in the east. I hated it.

I hated the snooty institution with so many insecure grad students with their Marxist thrusts and other ridiculous affectations, with their barely concealed meanness, and the pipe-smoking professors out of touch with my sad ass. Many of them were fine but not all of them and the ones who weren't sickened me. There was such a disconnect between the fabled ivy tower and daily American life as sweated by regular American guys like me, not to mention estranged Chicanos flashing by that I needed to get out of there.

Plus the snow sucked. Before I left I got a job at a bagel shop smearing cream cheese on assorted toasted bagels when not driving batches around to other shops and offices in the upstate New York area. (Ithaca, New York, Cornell University: there, my CV, remnants from my bio, and the fourth wall smashed with my brown fist offering you a bagel, friend. I made a good bagel!)

So I carried my newly found skills to Fresno, the place we settled in, and made bread rise out of nothing and conducted the local black-tie symphony orchestra on the lawn of the Courthouse Square in front of a crowd of thousands. They were wearing overalls and the occasional Mexican in peasant rags approached me for a peso and I gave him none.

I had none. Just my music.

William Saroyan crept out of his own shadow lurking under the huge statue of himself set up in the corner, and ventured toward me. He danced a two-step and retreated.

"Saroyan!" I shouted to the crowd and folded my baton. More like broke the motherfucker over my head and descended the podium all dazed and confused, leaving the crowd with a last number by Zeppelin.

They clapped, they roared and...

Our wheels got stuck in the mud. The wagon tilted to the side and while I helped the little lady down we really never got going in that town, we didn't. She got mired in the worst the university had to offer, the worst.

An earlier draft of this story goes:

She wore a sunbonnet and came out of the barn shielding her eyes from the sun. It was still too powerful and blinding for her to face alone. She thought she was something.

The bottles stacked up in a little pyramid in the kitchen for the recycling man. The recycling man never came. When a minor earthquake struck, she said, "Shit," and laughed it off with a hangover, walking around with a draft of an unfinished paper in one hand, a glass of wine in the other. She said, "Listen to this, it's my new paper."

But I would like to end with a fairy tale:

Once upon a time there was a beautiful princess and an ugly old toad. The ugly old toad was recognizable as a certain Chicano known to you. She kissed him and he turned into the handsome prince, kneeling by her bedside in the gold-curtained room, which was on the seventh floor of the Fresno hospital where she ended up after she cracked up.[2]

That's because her paper remained incomplete.[3] It stopped in mid-sentence and just kind of hung there...[4]

For three or four years while she got involved in department politics and a mess of bullshit that meant nothing to her or anybody finally.

"Giddyap!" I got on, all right. I found a job throwing newspapers in the mornings out of the back of the station wagon I had bought on borrowed money from my wife, another favor of hers,[5] and began...

TO WRITE, slowly but surely pick up the pieces as embarrassing as that sounds

Of my life.

Grooving, on a Sunday afternoon...

Everything was good, yeah? The message machine said so.

"Hi, we'll have a late dinner. I'm off to the university for a meeting about everything. The department is in turmoil. Bye, take care of Ben. Love you, Ben!" Beep.

She came home one Monday beaten and tortured, a noose around her neck and whip burns on her arms and back.

They had tied her to a pole and lashed her with fifty good, long strokes to the horror and delight of her department where she had gotten

TOO COCKY.

Taking it in her mouth her butt it was good

Night señorita the compañero said to the frog and tipped his sombrero and left

Home again.[6]

ENDNOTES TO *The World Came Crashing Down On My Wife*

[1] Oh yes it was. The despair was real. Broken homes, broken lives in that large, windowless room behind that door, brown and plain, that my son pointed to one night while visiting her and said, "That's the bad room, isn't it? The bad room?"

That's where they spoke their group stuff. He could sense the vibes from the hall. In a department meeting, lonely and cold, she had to listen to a man brutalize her for thirty minutes before he wrapped it up with a hard slap on the table.

Nervous embarrassment filled the room. A few cleared throats documented the unease.

They all loved it, though, the men in that room out to get a good woman, a strong woman.

"And the birth of a new woman followed; and it was all God's will," another draft said, "all part of God's plan."

In a portentous moment I said (listen to this! But don't fault me too much for the sins of my literary fathers. Writers came before me who wrote the same way. One of them even won a Nobel Prize. I think I'M DESERVING OF A NOBEL PRIZE. At least a small medal pinned to my chest):

So found her way west, wasting, in that goddamn fucking bottle, until God saw fit to humble her, yes humble her, in his own sweet time. But first he used her to his good end: and thrust her into a room full of men and women, liberals in name, male and female colleagues of hers: and made her the center stage attraction in a fierce battle on affirmative action that she won, but that shattered her, literally, and made her question her whole life, and hold up that bottle and say, "This is shit, you are rotten," in the hard light of understanding, "just like half the members of my department, scared of their own convictions, not even knowing their own convictions."

In an act of bravery...

Then looked at me and said, "Are you with me?"

"Yes. What happened in that room?"

"They set me up for the fall."

"You were full of pride and arrogance."

"Yes, but they were so cowardly, nobody could stop a madman, an—"

"Injustice—"

"Yes."

"—from taking place."

And that is what happened.

An injustice took place in a department meeting where she was allowed to be battered mercilessly. She was shamelessly attacked.

It was just plain ugly. A malicious man with a history of confrontation got the upper hand. He was given free rein to do what he wanted with a too-fresh faculty member, an out-of-line young woman.

He did his best to break her, simply, an egoistic graybeard named Simpson who had made a stand against the great and mighty ADMINISTRATION twenty years ago and been treated badly. That was in the sixties. He had been taught the limits of power, and now he distrusted anybody shaking his own power base without his consent, without his, how should I put it? permission.

THE WORLD CAME CRASHING DOWN ON MY WIFE

He was notoriously paranoid of anybody advocating anything new, especially of anybody in favor of minorities who he, like the rest of the department, distrusted immensely. The idea of them actually made the body cringe. Minorities. They couldn't be as good as us, ever. Affirmative action raged, and he snarled back. "Well, then..."

She sat at the long rectangular table in the conference room while he laid in to her. He attacked her for half an hour in the most damning, vicious language the department had ever heard. He ranted and raved at her until he brought her to the edge of tears.

It was so ugly a female colleague shook in the hall afterward. But she didn't break, she didn't cave.

It was the worst thing a few others had seen in their personal lives. It was academic madness.

A little fat man waving around a paper ruled the floor and held the men spellbound. Their hero!

Then she gathered herself. She breathed in deeply and blew out her breath and took the floor again.

She wasn't through yet. She had her right to speak under Robert's Rules of Order, *the department bible.*

"Are you done, Simpson?"

"Yes."

"Then I would like to address a few issues you brought up, point by point, to show the fallacies and illogic of your thinking, the deep-seated phobias against this black candidate permeating your argument, phobias based on stereotypes, assumptions and biases so naked and blatant that, frankly, I'm going to embarrass you, Simpson, you and all your demented cronies in this sad excuse for a department, a gathering of seemingly mature and intellectually honest men and women, let alone capable. I'm going to teach you to think. I'm going to give you a lesson in reasoning. But before I do that, might I add that you, Professor Lawson, as department chair have so abrogated your duties in allowing this madman to rant and rave at me for thirty-eight minutes unstopped while you barely contained a self-satisfied smirk in the corner, setting a new low for what I thought were agreed upon standards of human decency in this department, in how we treat each other in and out of meetings, that I may file a grievance against you. No, no, I won't hear it now. I have the floor. Let's look at Simpson's arguments. One," she took a sip of water, and I heard she was magnificent.

I heard she stunned with the quality of her mind at work, on display.

But we go back to the hospital now:

"But you are here?"

"Yes."

"And you won?"

"Yes."

"That's all that matters, baby," and I grabbed her hand and cried...

[2] Oh shucks shall I leave that out the hospital scene, the whole background to her breakdown, or take it out, I mean or leave it in, go minimalist or what? Tell me, man, tell me! I can't make decisions anymore, I can't! My thesis, entitled *The End of All Things Human and Other Raw Jokes*, got a few chuckles from my creative writing committee, fine men and great talents supporting a poor emotionally undone person like me. I stood on the table and bared my chest! I ripped open my Ivy League shirt and pointed to my heart! It was real! It was pumping! Thump-a-thump-thump

through my brown chest it pounded! You could see it stretching the skin so tight I grimaced! That was a year later when I returned to defend my thesis and get out of there, officially, with a sheepskin in hand. "Baa-bye," were my final words to my committee I really did respect, and I appreciated all she had done for me, supporting my sad ass while I wrote...while I finished up...I hung the MFA on the wall at home. *"If not for you,"* I played Bob Dylan in the background to commemorate her role in it, *"I couldn't even find the door."*

[3] Horseshit, sentimental horseshit, experimental claptrap. I have decided right this minute that the best place for these notes is at the back of the story, not in the middle where they get in the way of the narrative. This comes after much agonizing over everything, over every aspect of this story including the design which is out of my hands because it'll probably never see print unless some freakish editor like Mannheim Steinberg picks it up for his underground journal UNDERGROUND JOURNAL which you can't find anywhere because it's underground and if you could it wouldn't be. Fucking Mannheim sent me a postcard with postage due asking me for more shit the last time I sent him a story. Coffee-stained and abrupt, the note mentioned losing my previous manuscript in the office, which he just got evicted from. "PLEASE SEND TO THIS ADDRESS." Then blank. I wanted to cry when I saw that because I had been crying recently. It tore me up that some people didn't have a place to stay. Homeless bastards scrounging around litter-filled trashcans on the outskirts of Fresno. Big grins on derelict faces waking up to morning sunshine on my newspaper route. Living poems they are. Providing some consolation in life. Ah, me! She came out of the hospital in a wheelchair, bundled in a blanket. I picked her up at the entrance and put her in the car. We drove home silently down Fresno streets alive with Christmas. Lights hung on roofs, and fog shrouded the houses. *"Si-lent night."* Christmas carols reached us from a sweet group of kids moving down the street. *"Ho-ly night..."*

[4] Like me, doing my work, though, all right? Getting to know the scene a little bit, the creative writing scene in town, centered around... the unnameable, the ineffable... PETER GODOY! POET EXTRAORDINAIRE! I risk blasphemy by spelling his name.

[5] That worked for a while before I moved on to another gig in town, another splendid shit job giving me at least a few honest dollars I could call my own. I needed spending money to drink in bars frequented by suicidal priests and write in cafes so dimly lit only William Saroyan's luminous presence saved my eyes. I hunched over torn manuscripts and made brave starts with a few daring utterances: *Under the sun at noon he took off his shirt and howled like a coyote lost in the desert, seeking the pack scattered over the stony wastes. Sometimes in the life of a coyote, he realizes he's lonely. Ow-ow-ow-wooooo!* Or my personal favorite, a riff on the working class, which was big around here, big. *The working class was so full of shit it was hard to take seriously, but as he was one of them, indisputably stamped with the moronic gestures and attitudes of that beaten group of modern peasants still too dumb to see its way out of its misery, perpetually recycling itself with stupid anti-intellectualism he couldn't stomach—he was, after all, an intellectual of sorts, albeit a sloppy one, and not immune to certain currents of thought in the air—he walked warily among them, knowing he was a goddamn hypocrite if he claimed anything more than an ambivalent relationship to the frustrating bastards. He loved them, he hated them. But when he wrote about them, he was one of the best in America at it. He knew how full of shit they were, just like him.*

Then I wrote a crazy story about apt shit like...

You know, the working class...

"Fuck you."

"FUCK YOU."

I sent it in to the anthology entitled *The Pickaxe and the Hoe, the Best of the Valley Voices,* and got roundly rejected. People thought I lacked polish. They were right. I do.

Comments ranged from "mildly amusing" to "atrocious." Peter Godoy himself weighed in with a stinging rejection: "Lacks maturity and distinction. Not what we're looking for. I wish I could be more helpful, but it stinks." Then they published the same old crap about the downtrodden bastards we are, the working class.

I couldn't find evidence of this species anywhere. I saw a bundle of nerves and anger everywhere I turned.

Well, fuck me. *Así estaba la cosa.*

But I couldn't let them get away with treating a genius so ruthlessly.

I sent them a curt note demanding my rights: "In the anthology!" Then I protested at the offices of the press with a sign of William Saroyan held up high and proudly. He nodded approvingly every time I looked up.

He was glad to be alive again.

All right? Do you get that loud and clear?

Rage, rage against the dying of the light! All right? I wrote that myself right now.

All right?

Can you see the real me, can you?

The Who, I saw them in concert once, years ago, in Los Angeles. It was a good show. Thousands of kids stood up on their tiptoes and lifted tiny blue flames to the sky and shouted: "More, more! Yeah!"

I imagine they're shouting for me now. I just want to be loved, don't you?

[6] The world came crashing down on my wife, man, I was there, too, huddled under the rubble. We stayed there for a season, and then split. When the rains came pouring down, and the sun shone mightily, we held each other and laughed, so happy to be alive.

Song for You

For my son

I want to sing a little song, write a little song, for Fresno, before I leave. Ground her in the love I have for my son. Song for you, Benny boy, here it comes.

Something simple and embarrassingly sweet is in the air. We're hanging around at home, doing nothing but our morning thing again, me sitting at the kitchen table with a newspaper, and a coffee cup in hand, and you, Benny boy, toddling curiously.

You're opening cabinets and sticking your head in.

"Hey, Benny! Let's go to the Manchester Mall and get on the horses! I'll strap you in your stroller and take you across Blackstone today! We'll ride them like cowboys on the plains! Or race them! Hear them? They're waiting for us, Benny boy, they're neighing!"

Song for you, Benny boy, that's the way it went.

We headed to the carousel in the mall. We crossed Blackstone just like I promised, looking both ways, you with a sunshade protecting your fair skin, your lighter- than-me olive flesh, and me pushing the stroller with a Lakers Championship tee shirt on. We beat those Celtics! We tore them up!

Song for you, Benny boy! It's springtime and beautiful! I buy tickets for us at the makeshift booth in the mall. It's got colored balloons painted on it and a few spirited horses running across the sky with gay clowns waving at us.

It's got a fence around it.

"There they are, Benny boy, there they are!"

We get on the big brown horse with the golden saddle.
Nostrils flaring, eyes wide, he's fierce and ready, head flung
back, to race! Big teeth snap at the air. A silver bit keeps him
in check. We've got the reins!

"Here we go, Benny, here we go!" The music starts.

The horses move! Up and down we go sharing a saddle, me
on the rump of the horse, really, and you clutching the pole,
with glistening, merry eyes. "Go, Benny, go, race you to the
finish!" You fling your head back and laugh so hard the janitor
stops and smiles and waves, holding a dustpan and sweeper.
We smile and wave back.

"See her, Benny? Smile back at the nice lady! La señora!
Wave bye to her!"

The merry-go-round takes us away.

"Okay, here we go again!" We round the bend and see the
benches where the old men sit holding canes between their
knees, so sad, but smiling, too, at us!

Song for you, Benny boy, just for you.

That's the way it was, Benny boy, just like that.

STEPHEN D. GUTIERREZ

Stephen D. Gutierrez is the author of *Elements*, winner of the Nilon Award (FC2), and *Live from Fresno y Los*, winner of an American Book Award sponsored by the Before Columbus Foundation. *The Mexican Man in His Backyard* completes his trilogy of essays and stories. Gutierrez's stories and essays have been published in many magazines and anthologies, and he has produced plays in the San Francisco Bay Area and in upstate New York. Originally from Los Angeles, he now lives in the San Francisco Bay Area, where he teaches at California State University East Bay. He and his wife Jacqueline Doyle, a writer and professor, have a grown son, Benjamin. For more, go to STEPHENDGUTIERREZ.COM.